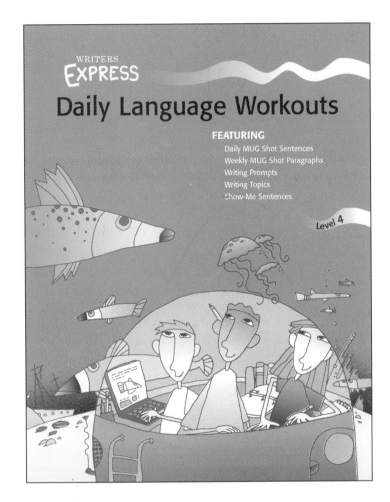

WRITERS EXPRESS

Daily Language Workouts

FEATURING
Daily MUG Shot Sentences
Weekly MUG Shot Paragraphs
Writing Prompts
Writing Topics
Show-Me Sentences

Level 4

Daily language and writing practice for

Grade 4

WRITE SOURCE®

GREAT SOURCE EDUCATION GROUP
a Houghton Mifflin Company
Wilmington, Massachusetts
www.greatsource.com

A Few Words About *Daily Language Workouts 4*

Before you begin . . .

The activities in this book will help your students build basic writing and language skills. You'll find three types of exercises on the following pages:

MUG Shot Sentences There are 175 sentences highlighting **m**echanics, **u**sage, and/or **g**rammar (MUG). There's one sentence for every day of the school year. For the first 18 weeks, focused sentences usually concentrate on one skill per week. Then the sentences for the final 17 weeks present a mixed review of errors, and students are asked to correct several types of errors in each sentence.

MUG Shot Paragraphs There are 35 weekly paragraphs. During the first 18 weeks, the paragraphs, like the sentences, usually focus on one type of mechanics, usage, or grammar error. The paragraphs for the final 17 weeks offer a mixed review of editing skills based on skills covered during each week of sentences.

Daily Writing Practice This section begins with **writing prompts** presented on pages that you can photocopy or place on an overhead projector. The prompts include thought-provoking topics and graphics designed to inspire expository, narrative, descriptive, persuasive, and creative writing. A discussion of daily journal writing introduces the lists of intriguing **writing topics**. Finally, the **Show-Me sentences** provide starting points for paragraphs, essays, and a wide variety of other writing forms.

Authors: Pat Sebranek and Dave Kemper

Printed in the United States of America

International Standard Book Number: 0-669-47434-7

3 4 5 6 7 8 9 10 -POO- 05 04 03 02

Table of Contents

Editing and Proofreading Marks

These symbols may be used to correct MUG Shot sentences and paragraphs.

Insert here.	$\wedge$	*them* take$_\wedge$home
Insert a comma, semicolon, or colon.	$\wedge$ $\wedge$ $\wedge$	Troy$_\wedge$Michigan
Insert a period.	$\odot$	Mrs$\odot$
Insert a hyphen.	$\overset{-}{\wedge}$	one$_\wedge$third cup
Insert a question mark or an exclamation point.	$\overset{?}{\wedge}$ $\overset{!}{\wedge}$	How about you$_\wedge$
Capitalize a letter.	$/$ (or) $\equiv$	Toronto (or) toronto
Make a capital letter lowercase.	$/$	h History
Replace or delete.	— (or) γ	*cold* a ~~hot~~ day (or) a ~~not~~ day (or) a ~~hot~~ day
Insert an apostrophe or quotation marks.	$\vee$ $\vee$ $\vee$	Bill's "Wow!"
Use italics.	_____	Tracker

MUG Shot
Sentences

The MUG Shot sentences are designed to be used at the beginning of each class period as a quick and efficient way to review **m**echanics, **u**sage, and **g**rammar. Each sentence can be corrected and discussed in 3 to 5 minutes.

MUG Shot Sentence Organizer

Name _____ Date_____

Corrected Sentence:

_____

_____

_____

Corrected Sentence:

_____

_____

_____

Corrected Sentence:

_____

_____

_____

Corrected Sentence:

_____

_____

_____

Corrected Sentence:

_____

_____

_____

Implementation and Evaluation

The first 18 weeks of MUG Shot sentences are focused sentences. The sentences for each week usually focus on one proofreading skill. The remaining 17 weeks of MUG Shot sentences provide mixed reviews of two or three different proofreading skills per sentence.

Implementation

On the days that you use MUG Shot sentences, we suggest that you have students **correct the sentence orally.** After you write the sentence on the board, be sure to read it aloud to be sure students understand the sentence. Write the corrections on the board as a volunteer provides them. (The student may use the proofreading marks on page iv.) Have the student explain his or her corrections and discuss the results. If you wish, then ask all students to write the corrected form in their notebooks.

You may also **write a sentence on the board** at the beginning of the class period. Allow students time to read the sentence to themselves. (Make sure they understand the sentence.) Then have students correct each MUG Shot in a space reserved for them in their notebooks (or on a copy of the "MUG Shot Sentence Organizer" provided on page 2 of this book). Students may be supplied with a copy of the "Editing and Proofreading Marks" on page iv as a guide for marking changes to their MUG Shot sentences. Be sure to read each sentence aloud before students begin. Then have students in pairs or as a class discuss their corrections. Also make sure that each student understands why the corrections were made.

Each Friday, review the MUG Shots covered for the week. You might assign the MUG Shot paragraph that contains errors similar to the type students have worked on for the week. (See page 75.)

Evaluation

If you assign sentences daily, evaluate your students' work at the end of each week. We recommend that you give them a basic performance score for their work. This performance score might be based on having each sentence for that week written correctly in their language arts notebooks. You might also have students reflect on their MUG Shot work in a brief freewriting at the end of the week, or have them correct one or two review sentences. Consider asking the students to submit sentences for this review activity.

Note: In the MUG Shot sentences showing corrections for run-on sentences, sentence fragments, and sentence combining, one possible correction is shown. However, there are often a number of possible answers that would also be correct.

WEEK 1: The End of the Line

■ **End Punctuation**

Mirrors actually show reverse images of objects

■ **End Punctuation**

Did you know that California was named after a character in a popular

Spanish novel

■ **End Punctuation**

Wake up, America—swing dancing is back

■ **End Punctuation**

Tell me the name of the first English colony

■ **End Punctuation**

An African elephant could flap up a strong breeze with those ears,

wouldn't you agree

WEEK 1: Corrected Sentences

■ End Punctuation

Mirrors actually show reverse images of objects.

■ End Punctuation

Did you know that California was named after a character in a popular

Spanish novel?

■ End Punctuation

Wake up, America—swing dancing is back! (or) .

■ End Punctuation

Tell me the name of the first English colony.

■ End Punctuation

An African elephant could flap up a strong breeze with those ears,

wouldn't you agree?

WEEK 2: Get in Line

■ Comma (Items in a Series)

The United States team at the first Olympics in 1896 consisted of seven runners a pole-vaulter a shot-putter and a hurdler.

■ Comma (Items in a Series)

On Saturday mornings, I watch cartoons eat breakfast help clean the house and wash the dog.

■ Comma (Items in a Series)

Here's a list of my least favorite vegetables: broccoli lima beans cauliflower beets and artichokes.

■ Comma (Items in a Series)

My favorite cars are high-powered sports cars hard-top convertibles and luxury-edition sport utility vehicles.

■ Comma (Items in a Series)

Anteaters have eyes ears noses and mouths, but no teeth.

WEEK 2: **Corrected Sentences**

■ **Comma (Items in a Series)**

The United States team at the first Olympics in 1896 consisted of seven

runners, a pole-vaulter, a shot-putter, and a hurdler.

■ **Comma (Items in a Series)**

On Saturday mornings, I watch cartoons, eat breakfast, help clean the

house, and wash the dog.

■ **Comma (Items in a Series)**

Here's a list of my least favorite vegetables: broccoli, lima beans,

cauliflower, beets, and artichokes.

■ **Comma (Items in a Series)**

My favorite cars are high-powered sports cars, hard-top convertibles, and

luxury-edition sport utility vehicles.

■ **Comma (Items in a Series)**

Anteaters have eyes, ears, noses, and mouths, but no teeth.

WEEK 3: Addressing the Issue

■ Comma (In Dates)

On June 16 1963 Valentina V. Tereshkova (a Russian) became the first woman to travel in outer space.

■ Comma (In Addresses)

Animal lovers may join Ranger Rick's Nature Club 8925 Leesburg Pike Vienna Virginia 22184.

■ Comma (In Dates)

On July 4 1776 the American colonies declared their independence from Great Britain.

■ Comma (In Dates)

The English first celebrated May Day as a day to honor workers on May 1 1890.

■ Comma (In Dates and In Addresses)

On June 25 1998 my family stayed in a motel at 5353 Midland Avenue Billings Montana.

WEEK 3: Corrected Sentences

■ Comma (In Dates)

On June 16,1963,Valentina V. Tereshkova (a Russian) became the first woman to travel in outer space.

■ Comma (In Addresses)

Animal lovers may join Ranger Rick's Nature Club,8925 Leesburg Pike, Vienna,Virginia 22184.

■ Comma (In Dates)

On July 4,1776,the American colonies declared their independence from Great Britain.

■ Comma (In Dates)

The English first celebrated May Day as a day to honor workers on May 1,1890.

■ Comma (In Dates and In Addresses)

On June 25,1998,my family stayed in a motel at 5353 Midland Avenue, Billings,Montana.

WEEK 4: A Number of Interruptions

- ## Comma (To Keep Numbers Clear and To Set Off Interjections)

  Hey if one centipede has 100 legs, do 100 centipedes have 100000 legs?

- ## Comma (To Keep Numbers Clear)

  A mile is just a mile unless it is 5280 feet, 1760 yards, or a little more than 1609 meters.

- ## Comma (To Keep Numbers Clear)

  The moon is only 2155 miles across, but the sun is 867000 miles across.

- ## Comma (To Keep Numbers Clear)

  Light travels at a speed of 186282 miles per second.

- ## Comma (To Keep Numbers Clear and To Set Off Interjections)

  A place in India once got 26466 millimeters of rain in a year. Wow that's 1042 inches!

WEEK 4: **Corrected Sentences**

■ **Comma (To Keep Numbers Clear and To Set Off Interjections)**

Hey, if one centipede has 100 legs, do 100 centipedes have 100,000 legs?

(Answer: No. They have 10,000 legs.)

■ **Comma (To Keep Numbers Clear)**

A mile is just a mile unless it is 5,280 feet, 1,760 yards, or a little more than 1,609 meters.

■ **Comma (To Keep Numbers Clear)**

The moon is only 2,155 miles across, but the sun is 867,000 miles across.

■ **Comma (To Keep Numbers Clear)**

Light travels at a speed of 186,282 miles per second.

■ **Comma (To Keep Numbers Clear and To Set Off Interjections)**

A place in India once got 26,466 millimeters of rain in a year. Wow, that's 1,042 inches!

WEEK 5: Pause for a ^an Independent Clause

■ Comma (Between Two Independent Clauses)

I have never been to Alaska so I have never seen Mt. McKinley.

■ Comma (Between Two Independent Clauses)

Most fish do not sleep but some types stand on their tails and lean against coral for a snooze.

■ Comma (Between Two Independent Clauses)

After the first harvest, the Pilgrims held a feast for they wanted to give God thanks.

■ Comma (Between Two Independent Clauses)

Andrew Jackson was born in South Carolina and he became the first man born in a log cabin to be elected president of the United States.

■ Comma (Between Two Independent Clauses)

Quicksand can suck animals down to their deaths but a person can escape by lying flat and rolling out.

WEEK 5: **Corrected Sentences**

- ### Comma (Between Two Independent Clauses)

  I have never been to Alaska, so I have never seen Mt. McKinley.

- ### Comma (Between Two Independent Clauses)

  Most fish do not sleep, but some types stand on their tails and lean against coral for a snooze.

- ### Comma (Between Two Independent Clauses)

  After the first harvest, the Pilgrims held a feast, for they wanted to give God thanks.

- ### Comma (Between Two Independent Clauses)

  Andrew Jackson was born in South Carolina, and he became the first man born in a log cabin to be elected president of the United States.

- ### Comma (Between Two Independent Clauses)

  Quicksand can suck animals down to their deaths, but a person can escape by lying flat and rolling out.

WEEK 6: Hyperlinks

■ Hyphen

Well informed football fans know that the Green Bay Packers beat the
Kansas City Chiefs in the first Super Bowl.

■ Hyphen

My great aunt had 18 children; one half were boys, and the other half
were girls.

■ Hyphen

The Beatles, a well known musical group, released 29 records in 1964.

■ Hyphen

The highest scoring basketball game ever occurred in 1983 when the
Detroit Pistons outscored the Denver Nuggets, 186-183.

■ Hyphen

I would guess that two thirds of the class knows that you cannot divide
a one syllable word at the end of a line.

WEEK 6: **Corrected Sentences**

- ## Hyphen

  Well-informed football fans know that the Green Bay Packers beat the

  Kansas City Chiefs in the first Super Bowl.

- ## Hyphen

  My great-aunt had 18 children; one-half were boys, and the other half

  were girls.

- ## Hyphen

  The Beatles, a well-known musical group, released 29 records in 1964.

- ## Hyphen

  The highest-scoring basketball game ever occurred in 1983 when the

  Detroit Pistons outscored the Denver Nuggets, 186-183.

- ## Hyphen

  I would guess that two-thirds of the class knows that you cannot divide

  a one-syllable word at the end of a line.

WEEK 7: It's All Yours

- **Apostrophe (In Contractions and In Possessives)**

  Although a flea isnt very big, the critters remarkable strength allows it to jump 200 times its length.

- **Apostrophe (In Possessives)**

  Koala bears main food is eucalyptus leaves.

- **Apostrophe (In Possessives)**

  Alexander Graham Bells first telephone was displayed in Philadelphias Exhibition Hall in 1876.

- **Apostrophe (In Possessives)**

  Harriet Beecher Stowes book *Uncle Toms Cabin* made people aware of the evils of slavery.

- **Apostrophe (In Possessives)**

  Charles Dickens books tell about his concern for the poor people of his day.

WEEK 7: **Corrected Sentences**

■ **Apostrophe (In Contractions and In Possessives)**

Although a flea isn't very big, the critters' remarkable strength allows it

to jump 200 times its length.

The cat's toys are yellow

■ **Apostrophe (In Possessives)**

Koala bears' main food is eucalyptus leaves.

■ **Apostrophe (In Possessives)**

Alexander Graham Bell's first telephone was displayed in Philadelphia's

Exhibition Hall in 1876.

■ **Apostrophe (In Possessives)**

Harriet Beecher Stowe's book *Uncle Tom's Cabin* made people aware of the

evils of slavery.

■ **Apostrophe (In Possessives)**

Dickens' (or) Dickens's
Charles ~~Dickens~~ books tell about his concern for the poor people of

his day.

WEEK 8: And I Quote . . .

■ Quotation Marks

When astronaut Neil Armstrong stepped onto the moon, he said, That's one small step for a man, one giant leap for mankind.

■ Quotation Marks

The skydiving instructor asked, Who wants to go first?

■ Quotation Marks

Writer Sandra Cisneros says this about school: I didn't like school because all they saw was the outside of me.

■ Quotation Marks

Was it Eleanor Roosevelt who said, You must do the thing you think you cannot do?

■ Quotation Marks

I always laugh when I read Shel Silverstein's poem Jumping Rope.

WEEK 8: **Corrected Sentences**

■ **Quotation Marks**

When astronaut Neil Armstrong stepped onto the moon, he said, "That's one small step for a man, one giant leap for mankind."

■ **Quotation Marks**

The skydiving instructor asked, "Who wants to go first?"

■ **Quotation Marks**

Writer Sandra Cisneros says this about school: "I didn't like school because all they saw was the outside of me."

■ **Quotation Marks**

Was it Eleanor Roosevelt who said, "You must do the thing you think you cannot do?"

■ **Quotation Marks**

I always laugh when I read Shel Silverstein's poem "Jumping Rope."

WEEK 9: Capital Idea!

- ## Capitalization

the address for the Football hall of fame is 2121 george halas drive, canton, ohio 44708.

- ## Capitalization

elijah mcCoy's parents escaped from slavery in kentucky many years before the civil war.

- ## Capitalization

today the people christopher columbus called indians are often called native americans.

- ## Capitalization

my dad and I marched in the st. patrick's day parade in chicago.

- ## Capitalization

jan e. matzeliger made the first shoe-stitching machine in the united states.

WEEK 9: Corrected Sentences

■ Capitalization

T   H F   G H D

the address for the Football hall of fame is 2121 george halas drive,

C   O

canton, ohio 44708.

■ Capitalization

E M   K

elijah mcCoy's parents escaped from slavery in Kentucky many years

              C W

before the civil war.

■ Capitalization

T   C   C   I

today the people christopher columbus called indians are often called

N A

native americans.

■ Capitalization

M   S P   D   C

my dad and I marched in the st. patrick's day parade in chicago.

■ Capitalization

J E M   U

jan e. matzeliger made the first shoe-stitching machine in the united

S

states.

WEEK 10: Geographically Speaking

■ **Capitalization**

The suez canal connects the mediterranean sea to the red sea.

■ **Capitalization**

many germans and scandinavians settled in the midwest.

■ **Capitalization**

The amazon river contains more water than the nile river, the mississippi river, and the yangtze river put together.

■ **Capitalization**

the empire state building in new york city is not as tall as the sears tower in chicago, illinois.

■ **Capitalization**

Would you rather visit redwood park in northern california or yosemite park in central california?

WEEK 10: **Corrected Sentences**

■ **Capitalization**

The ~~s~~**S**uez ~~c~~**C**anal connects the ~~m~~**M**editerranean ~~s~~**S**ea to the ~~r~~**R**ed ~~s~~**S**ea.

■ **Capitalization**

~~m~~**M**any ~~g~~**G**ermans and ~~s~~**S**candinavians settled in the ~~m~~**M**idwest.

■ **Capitalization**

The ~~a~~**A**mazon ~~r~~**R**iver contains more water than the ~~n~~**N**ile ~~r~~**R**iver, the ~~m~~**M**ississippi ~~r~~**R**iver, and the ~~y~~**Y**angtze ~~r~~**R**iver put together.

■ **Capitalization**

~~t~~**T**he ~~e~~**E**mpire ~~s~~**S**tate ~~b~~**B**uilding in ~~n~~**N**ew ~~y~~**Y**ork ~~c~~**C**ity is not as tall as the ~~s~~**S**ears ~~t~~**T**ower in ~~c~~**C**hicago, ~~i~~**I**llinois.

■ **Capitalization**

Would you rather visit ~~r~~**R**edwood ~~p~~**P**ark in northern ~~c~~**C**alifornia or ~~y~~**Y**osemite ~~p~~**P**ark in central ~~c~~**C**alifornia?

WEEK 11: One Is a Lonely Number

■ **Plurals**

We picked many bunch of flower to give to our moms

We grabbed our paintes and brushs and headed for the art room.

■ **Plurals**

My mother uses her sharpest knifes to cut the loafs of bread.

■ **Plurals**

Pianoes are popular because they can produce a wide range of soundes.

■ **Plurals**

My little brother enjoys chasing bunnys and gooses at the park.

■ **Plurals**

For supper, Mom prepared two platesful of tacoes and burritos.

WEEK 11: **Corrected Sentences**

■ Plurals

We grabbed our ~~paintes~~ *paints* and ~~brushs~~ *brushes* and headed for the art room.

■ Plurals

My mother uses her sharpest ~~knifes~~ *knives* to cut the ~~loafs~~ *loaves* of bread.

■ Plurals

Pianos
~~Pianoes~~ are popular because they can produce a wide range of ~~soundes~~ *sounds*.

■ Plurals

My little brother enjoys chasing ~~bunnys~~ *bunnies* and ~~gooses~~ *geese* at the park.

■ Plurals

For supper, Mom prepared two ~~platesful~~ *platefuls* of ~~tacoes~~ *tacos* and burritos.

WEEK 12: One Potato, Two Potato, Three Potato, Four

■ Numbers

The Pacific Ocean covers 64,000,000 square miles.

■ Numbers

Native Americans make up about one percent of the United States population; more than seven-hundred thousand Native Americans live in Oklahoma, California, and Arizona.

■ Numbers

By the year two thousand and twenty-five, experts think the population of the United States will be about three hundred million.

■ Numbers

About one out of every 5 people in the world is Chinese.

■ Numbers

31,000,000 people live in California, while only four-hundred thousand people live in Wyoming.

WEEK 12: **Corrected Sentences**

■ Numbers

64 million
The Pacific Ocean covers ~~64,000,000~~ square miles.

■ Numbers

1
Native Americans make up about ~~one~~ percent of the United States
700,000
population; more than ~~seven-hundred thousand~~ Native Americans live in

Oklahoma, California, and Arizona.

■ Numbers

2025
By the year ~~two thousand and twenty-five~~, experts think the population
300
of the United States will be about ~~three hundred~~ million.

■ Numbers

1
About ~~one~~ out of every 5 people in the world is Chinese.

■ Numbers

Thirty-one million   *400,000*
~~31,000,000~~ people live in California, while only ~~four-hundred thousand~~

people live in Wyoming.

WEEK 13: Reaching an Agreement

■ **Subject-Verb Agreement**

Cirrus clouds is the highest clouds in the sky.

are

■ **Subject-Verb Agreement**

Winter winds usually blows from north to south.

■ **Subject-Verb Agreement**

Sedimentary rocks is made of pieces of various types of rocks, minerals,

plants, or organisms.

are

■ **Subject-Verb Agreement**

Nobody know who invented eyeglasses, but they is very useful.

knows

■ **Subject-Verb Agreement**

The air in tornadoes spin in a circle.

WEEK 13: **Corrected Sentences**

- ## Subject-Verb Agreement

    are
    Cirrus clouds ~~is~~ the highest clouds in the sky.

- ## Subject-Verb Agreement

    blow
    Winter winds usually ~~blows~~ from north to south.

- ## Subject-Verb Agreement

    are
    Sedimentary rocks ~~is~~ made of pieces of various types of rocks, minerals,

    plants, or organisms.

- ## Subject-Verb Agreement

    knows   *are*
    Nobody ~~know~~ who invented eyeglasses, but they ~~is~~ very useful.

- ## Subject-Verb Agreement

    spins
    The air in tornadoes ~~spin~~ in a circle.

WEEK 14: Yes, I Agree

■ Subject-Verb Agreement

Eagles, pelicans, and trumpeter swans has been seen in Yellowstone National Park.

■ Subject-Verb Agreement

New York, New Jersey, and Pennsylvania is called the Middle Atlantic States.

■ Subject-Verb Agreement

Were Christopher Columbus or Vasco da Gama a greater explorer?

■ Subject-Verb Agreement

Either my mother or my grandparents comes to my soccer games.

■ Subject-Verb Agreement

There are a dogsled race each year in Alaska from Anchorage to Nome.

WEEK 14: **Corrected Sentences**

- ### Subject-Verb Agreement

  Eagles, pelicans, and trumpeter swans ~~has~~ *have* been seen in Yellowstone

  National Park.

- ### Subject-Verb Agreement

  New York, New Jersey, and Pennsylvania ~~is~~ *are* called the Middle Atlantic

  States.

- ### Subject-Verb Agreement

  Was
  ~~Were~~ Christopher Columbus or Vasco da Gama a greater explorer?

- ### Subject-Verb Agreement

  Either my mother or my grandparents ~~comes~~ *come* to my soccer games.

- ### Subject-Verb Agreement

  There ~~are~~ *is* a dogsled race each year in Alaska from Anchorage to Nome.

WEEK 15: Runaway Sentences

- **Run-On Sentence**

Pocahontas saved the life of John Smith she later married another settler.

- **Run-On Sentence**

A triathlon is a three-part race it includes swimming, running, and biking.

- **Run-On Sentence**

Russia is the largest country in the world Canada is the second largest.

- **Run-On Sentence**

On September 6, 1995, Cal Ripken broke one of baseball's most amazing records he played his 2,131st straight game.

- **Run-On Sentence**

What is the Liberty Bell why is it important?

WEEK 15: **Corrected Sentences**

■ Run-On Sentence

Pocahontas saved the life of John Smith, *but* she later married another settler.

■ Run-On Sentence

A triathlon is a three-part race. It includes swimming, running, and biking.

■ Run-On Sentence

Russia is the largest country in the world. Canada is the second largest.

■ Run-On Sentence

On September 6, 1995, Cal Ripken broke one of baseball's most amazing records. He played his 2,131st straight game.

■ Run-On Sentence

What is the Liberty Bell? Why is it important?

WEEK 16: Bits and Pieces

■ **Sentence Fragment**

An example of a kind person.

■ **Sentence Fragment**

Nervously waited for my friend to show up.

■ **Sentence Fragment**

Down the driveway, across the yard, over the fence, and through the alley.

■ **Sentence Fragment**

The person in my family with the best sense of humor.

■ **Sentence Fragment**

Gathered up my books by my locker.

WEEK 16: **Corrected Sentences** *(Answers will vary.)*

■ **Sentence Fragment**

Mr. Gardner is
An example of a kind person.

■ **Sentence Fragment**

I n
Nervously waited for my friend to show up.

■ **Sentence Fragment**

The dog chased my cat
Down the driveway, across the yard, over the fence, and through the

alley.

■ **Sentence Fragment**

The person in my family with the best sense of humor *is my sister Hillary.*

■ **Sentence Fragment**

After school, I
Gathered up my books by my locker.

WEEK 17: The Right Way

■ Using the Right Word

Their is know real reason why painters where white, but they almost always due.

■ Using the Right Word

Dogs tilt there heads to the side too here you're voice.

■ Using the Right Word

Principles are people with strong principals.

■ Using the Right Word

Hour science teacher is going two learn us about the whole in the ozone layer.

■ Using the Right Word

Sum stationary seams too pretty too right on.

WEEK 17: **Corrected Sentences**

■ Using the Right Word

There *no*   *wear*
~~Their~~ is ~~know~~ real reason why painters ~~where~~ white, but they almost

   do
always ~~due.~~

■ Using the Right Word

    their   *to hear your*
Dogs tilt ~~there~~ heads to the side ~~too~~ ~~here~~ ~~you're~~ voice.

■ Using the Right Word

Principals   *principles*
~~Principles~~ are people with strong ~~principals.~~

■ Using the Right Word

Our   *to teach*   *hole*
~~Hour~~ science teacher is going ~~two~~ ~~learn~~ us about the ~~whole~~ in the ozone

layer.

■ Using the Right Word

Some stationery seems   *to write*
~~Sum~~ ~~stationary~~ ~~seams~~ too pretty ~~too~~ ~~right~~ on.

WEEK 18: A Combination of Factors

■ Combining Sentences

Math was very hard yesterday, Math was very hard today. I'm going to ask for special help.

■ Combining Sentences

Earth orbits our sun. Eight other planets orbit our sun.

■ Combining Sentences

Everyone likes cute, furry animals. Naturalists even like spiders and insects.

■ Combining Sentences

One American mile equals 5,280 feet. One American mile equals 1,609.3 meters.

■ Combining Sentences

Lobsters have large claws. Lobsters run backward. Lobsters taste good when cooked and buttered.

WEEK 18: **Corrected Sentences** *(Answers may vary.)*

■ **Combining Sentences**

Math was very hard yesterday, ~~Math was very hard~~ *and* today, *so* I'm going to

ask for special help.

■ **Combining Sentences**

Earth ~~orbits our sun.~~ *and* Eight other planets orbit our sun.

■ **Combining Sentences**

Everyone likes cute, furry animals, *but* Naturalists even like spiders and

insects.

■ **Combining Sentences**

One American mile equals 5,280 feet. ~~One American mile equals~~ *or* 1,609.3

meters.

■ **Combining Sentences**

Lobsters have large claws, ~~Lobsters~~ run backward, *and* ~~Lobsters~~ taste good

when cooked and buttered.

WEEK 19: History of Language

■ **Using the Right Word, Capitalization, Numbers**

Their are twenty-six letters in the english alphabet.

■ **Comma (To Set Off Introductory Phrases and Clauses), Verb (Irregular), Pronoun-Antecedent Agreement**

At one time in its history the Greeks writed from right to left.

■ **Sentence Problems ("Of" for "Have"), Capitalization**

The semites could of been the first people to use pictures as words.

■ **Capitalization, Comma (To Set Off Appositives)**

The egyptians invented hieroglyphics a kind of picture writing 5,000 years ago.

■ **Capitalization, Subject-Verb Agreement, Run-On Sentence**

Today, deaf people uses Sign language they use it to talk to other people.

WEEK 19: **Corrected Sentences**

- **Using the Right Word, Capitalization, Numbers**

  There   *26*   *E*
  ~~Their~~ are ~~twenty-six~~ letters in the ~~e~~nglish alphabet.

- **Comma (To Set Off Introductory Phrases and Clauses), Verb (Irregular), Pronoun-Antecedent Agreement**

                their   *wrote*
  At one time in ~~its~~ history, the Greeks ~~writed~~ from right to left.

- **Sentence Problems ("Of" for "Have"), Capitalization**

      S   *have*
  The ~~s~~emites could ~~of~~ been the first people to use pictures as words.

- **Capitalization, Comma (To Set Off Appositives)**

      E
  The ~~e~~gyptians invented hieroglyphics, a kind of picture writing, 5,000

  years ago.

- **Capitalization, Subject-Verb Agreement, Run-On Sentence**

              use s   *T*
  Today, deaf people ~~uses~~ ~~s~~ign language. they use it to talk to other people.

WEEK 20: The English Language

- **Verb (Irregular), Capitalization, Comma (Items in a Series)**

  English was spoke only by people in the British Isles until the british empire spread the language to america africa australia and the Far East.

- **Comma (To Set Off Introductory Phrases and Clauses), Pronoun-Antecedent Agreement**

  Because English is spoken throughout the world they is being called the first global language.

- **Numbers, Subject-Verb Agreement**

  The English language have more words (close to 1,000,000) than the German language (only one hundred and eighty-five thousand).

- **Apostrophe (In Possessives), Adjective (Comparative/Superlative), Numbers**

  Of all the worlds two thousand and seven hundred languages, English has the most richest vocabulary.

- **Hyphen, Comma (In Direct Address), Verb (Irregular)**

  Diane did you know three fourths of the world's mail today is writed in English?

WEEK 20: **Corrected Sentences**

- ### Verb (Irregular), Capitalization, Comma (Items in a Series)

  English was ~~spoke~~ *spoken* only by people in the British Isles until the *B*/british
  E/empire spread the language to /*A*/america, /*A*/africa, /*A*/australia, and the Far East.

- ### Comma (To Set Off Introductory Phrases and Clauses), Pronoun-Antecedent Agreement

  Because English is spoken throughout the world, *it* ~~they~~ is being called the

  first global language.

- ### Numbers, Subject-Verb Agreement

  The English language ~~have~~ *has* more words (close to ~~1,000,000~~ *1 million*) than the

  German language (only ~~one hundred and eighty-five thousand~~ *185,000*).

- ### Apostrophe (In Possessives), Adjective (Comparative/Superlative), Numbers

  Of all the worlds' ~~two thousand and seven hundred~~ *2,700* languages, English

  has the ~~most~~ richest vocabulary.

- ### Hyphen, Comma (In Direct Address), Verb (Irregular)

  Diane, did you know three-fourths of the world's mail today is ~~writed~~ *written* in

  English?

WEEK 21: Something Fishy

- ## Comma (To Set Off Interjections), Numbers, Using the Right Word

  Wow a female herring lies 30 thousand eggs at once!

- ## Pronoun-Antecedent Agreement, Apostrophe (In Possessives), Comma (In Direct Address)

  Shelly did you know that the male sea horse protects the mothers eggs by keeping it in a pouch on his stomach?

- ## Using the Right Word, Semicolon, Adjective (Comparative/Superlative)

  One of the most unusualest fish is the flounder both eyes are on one side of it's body.

- ## Plurals, Semicolon

  The archerfish knocks insects off leafs it shoots a stream of water at them.

- ## Comma (Between Two Independent Clauses and To Separate Adjectives), Pronoun-Antecedent Agreement

  Tropical fish must live in clear warm water or it will die.

WEEK 21: **Corrected Sentences**

- ## Comma (To Set Off Interjections), Numbers, Using the Right Word

  Wow,*a* female herring ~~lies~~ *lays* ~~30 thousand~~ *30,000* eggs at once!

- ## Pronoun-Antecedent Agreement, Apostrophe (In Possessives), Comma (In Direct Address)

  Shelly,*did* you know that the male sea horse protects the mother*'*s eggs

  by keeping ~~it~~ *them* in a pouch on his stomach?

- ## Using the Right Word, Semicolon, Adjective (Comparative/Superlative)

  One of the most ~~unusualest~~ *unusual* fish is the flounder*;* both eyes are on one

  side of ~~it's~~ *its* body.

- ## Plurals, Semicolon

  The archerfish knocks insects off ~~leafs~~ *leaves*; it shoots a stream of water at

  them.

- ## Comma (Between Two Independent Clauses and To Separate Adjectives), Pronoun-Antecedent Agreement

  Tropical fish must live in clear,*warm* water,*or* ~~it~~ *they* will die.

WEEK 22: Animals on Parade

■ **Plurals, Using the Right Word, Rambling Sentence**

Kangarooes are amazing animals who live in Australia and can really jump and large ones can cover more then 30 feet with one leap!

■ **Adjective (Comparative/Superlative), Capitalization, Hyphen**

My five year old golden Retriever is the most calm dog in all of dade county.

■ **Using the Right Word, Spelling**

Female black widow spiders have poisenous bites and sometimes kill there mates.

■ **Using the Right Word, Subject-Verb Agreement**

A few animals sea in color, but most animals sees only shades of gray.

■ **Colon, Using the Right Word, Comma (Items in a Series)**

Movies have been maid from the following books Babe: The Gallant Pig Stuart Little The Iron Giant and The Borrowers.

WEEK 22: Corrected Sentences

■ Plurals, Using the Right Word, Rambling Sentence

Kangaroos
~~Kangarooes~~ are amazing animals ~~who~~ *that* live in Australia. ~~and~~ *They* can really

jump, and large ones can cover more ~~then~~ *than* 30 feet with one leap!

■ Adjective (Comparative/Superlative), Capitalization, Hyphen

My five-year-old golden *R*etriever is the ~~most calm~~ *calmest* dog in all of *D*ade

*C*ounty.

■ Using the Right Word, Spelling

Female black widow spiders have ~~poisenous~~ *poisonous* bites and sometimes kill

their
~~there~~ mates.

■ Using the Right Word, Subject-Verb Agreement

A few animals ~~sea~~ *see* in color, but most animals ~~sees~~ *see* only shades of gray.

■ Colon, Using the Right Word, Comma (Items in a Series)

Movies have been ~~maid~~ *made* from the following books: Babe: The Gallant Pig,

Stuart Little, The Iron Giant, and The Borrowers.

WEEK 23: Maps, Maps, Maps

- **Capitalization, Comma (Items in a Series and To Set Off Appositives)**

  The Gulf Stream a warm ocean current flows from the gulf of mexico past the east coast of Florida to the North Atlantic Ocean.

- **Comma (In Direct Address), Subject-Verb Agreement, Plurals**

  John seas is large bodys of salt water partly surrounded by land.

- **Quotation Marks, Comma (To Set Off Dialogue), Period**

  Mr Baily said Look up the Galápagos Islands on your maps and write down their latitude and longitude.

- **Capitalization, Run-On Sentence, Spelling**

  In 1849, a great flood of setlers headed west they followed a map of oregon and california made in 1848.

- **Comma (To Set Off Introductory Phrases and Clauses), Spelling, Apostrophe (In Contractions)**

  If you find the Great Lakes on a map youll see four of them share thier borders with Canada and the United States.

WEEK 23: **Corrected Sentences**

- ## Capitalization, Comma (Items in a Series and To Set Off Appositives)

The Gulf Stream, a warm ocean current, flows from the *G*ulf of *M*exico,

past the east coast of Florida, to the North Atlantic Ocean.

- ## Comma (In Direct Address), Subject-Verb Agreement, Plurals

John, seas ~~is~~ *are* large ~~bodys~~ *bodies* of salt water partly surrounded by land.

- ## Quotation Marks, Comma (To Set Off Dialogue), Period

Mr. Baily said, "Look up the Galápagos Islands on your maps and write

down their latitude and longitude."

- ## Capitalization, Run-On Sentence, Spelling

In 1849, a great flood of ~~setlers~~ *settlers* headed west. *T*hey followed a map of

*O*regon and *C*alifornia made in 1848.

- ## Comma (To Set Off Introductory Phrases and Clauses), Spelling, Apostrophe (In Contractions)

If you find the Great Lakes on a map, you'll see four of them share ~~thier~~ *their*

borders with Canada and the United States.

WEEK 24: On a Map . . .

■ **Using the Right Word, Comma (To Keep Numbers Clear), Capitalization**

They're more than 7100 islands that make up the country called the philippines.

■ **Using the Right Word, Capitalization, Semicolon**

The equator goes from East to West it passes threw South America and Africa.

■ **Italics and Underlining, Sentence Fragment, Comma (In Direct Address)**

Did you know that the Caspian Sea is actually a lake Tom? The world's largest saltwater lake (the word sea means a great body of salty water).

■ **Capitalization, Run-On Sentence, Apostrophe (In Possessives)**

Minnesota has the largest scandinavian population in the United States Duluth, on the shores of lake superior, is the countrys largest inland port.

■ **Comma (To Set Off Introductory Phrases and Clauses), Double Subjects, Using the Right Word**

Before reading this sentence did you know that the capitol of Canada it is Ottawa?

WEEK 24: **Corrected Sentences**

- **Using the Right Word, Comma (To Keep Numbers Clear), Capitalization**

There are
~~They're~~ more than 7,100 islands that make up the country called the

P
~~p~~hilippines.

- **Using the Right Word, Capitalization, Semicolon**

e   *w*   *through*
The equator goes from ~~E~~ast to ~~W~~est; it passes ~~threw~~ South America and

Africa.

- **Italics and Underlining, Sentence Fragment, Comma (In Direct Address)**

It's t
Did you know that the Caspian Sea is actually a lake, Tom? ~~T~~he world's

largest saltwater lake (the word <u>sea</u> means a great body of salty water).

- **Capitalization, Run-On Sentence, Apostrophe (In Possessives)**

S
Minnesota has the largest ~~s~~candinavian population in the United States.

L   *S*
Duluth, on the shores of ~~l~~ake ~~s~~uperior, is the country's largest inland port.

- **Comma (To Set Off Introductory Phrases and Clauses), Double Subjects, Using the Right Word**

capital
Before reading this sentence, did you know that the ~~capitol~~ of Canada ~~it~~

is Ottawa?

WEEK 25: Where in the World?

- **Sentence Fragment, Numbers**

  Canada a large country with a small population of 27,000,000 people.

- **Comma (To Keep Numbers Clear and To Separate Adjectives), Apostrophe (In Possessives)**

  Chinas first emperor was buried with an army of 7500 life-sized clay soldiers.

- **Using the Right Word, Semicolon, Adjective (Comparative/Superlative)**

  The Sahara Dessert may be the most hottest place on earth it holds the record temperature of 136.4 degrees Fahrenheit.

- **Using the Right Word, Comma (To Set Off Appositives)**

  The Czech Republic and Slovakia two of the newest nations in the world used too be called Czechoslovakia.

- **Comma (To Set Off Introductory Phrases and Clauses), Capitalization, Subject-Verb Agreement**

  When you is at the north pole the only direction you can go is South.

WEEK 25: **Corrected Sentences**

- **Sentence Fragment, Numbers**

Canada ∧ a large country with a small population of 27,000,000 people.
[above: *is*] [above 27,000,000: *27 million*]

- **Comma (To Keep Numbers Clear and To Separate Adjectives), Apostrophe (In Possessives)**

Chinas first emperor was buried with an army of 7,500 life-sized clay
[apostrophe inserted in Chinas; commas inserted]

soldiers.

- **Using the Right Word, Semicolon, Adjective (Comparative/Superlative)**

The Sahara Dessert may be the most hottest place on earth ∧ it holds the
[above Dessert: *Desert*] [most crossed out] [semicolon inserted]

record temperature of 136.4 degrees Fahrenheit.

- **Using the Right Word, Comma (To Set Off Appositives)**

The Czech Republic and Slovakia ∧ two of the newest nations in the world ∧
[commas inserted]

used too be called Czechoslovakia.
[above too: *to*] [too crossed out]

- **Comma (To Set Off Introductory Phrases and Clauses), Capitalization, Subject-Verb Agreement**

When you is at the north pole ∧ the only direction you can go is South.
[above is: *are*] [N above north] [P above pole] [comma inserted] [S above South]

WEEK 26: Colors and Symbols

- **Comma (To Set Off Introductory Phrases and Clauses),
  Using the Right Word, Apostrophe (In Contractions)**

  If you lived in ancient Rome you couldnt where purple unless you were
  a member of the emperor's family.

- **Comma (To Set Off Appositives), Capitalization, Using the Right Word**

  At won time in French history, only the Princess could wear scarlet a
  bright read color.

- **Using the Right Word, Plurals**

  Because they're were no sidewalkes long ago, people would roll out a red
  carpet for the royal family's too walk on.

- **Plurals, Numbers, Sentence Fragment**

  Wonder why most countrys have 3 colores in their flags.

- **Quotation Marks, Double Negatives, Comma (To Set Off Dialogue)**

  Yesterday our teacher told us Class, some people say that Betsy Ross
  didn't never design the American flag; some say Francis Hopkinson did
  that.

WEEK 26: **Corrected Sentences**

■ **Comma (To Set Off Introductory Phrases and Clauses), Using the Right Word, Apostrophe (In Contractions)**

If you lived in ancient Rome‸you couldn't ~~where~~ *wear* purple unless you were

a member of the emperor's family.

■ **Comma (To Set Off Appositives), Capitalization, Using the Right Word**

At ~~won~~ *one* time in French history, only the *p*rincess could wear scarlet‸a

bright ~~read~~ *red* color.

■ **Using the Right Word, Plurals**

Because ~~they're~~ *there* were no ~~sidewalkes~~ *sidewalks* long ago, people would roll out a red

carpet for the royal ~~family's~~ *families* ~~too~~ *to* walk on.

■ **Plurals, Numbers, Sentence Fragment**

‸*I* *W*onder why most ~~countrys~~ *countries* have ~~3~~ *three* ~~colores~~ *colors* in their flags.

■ **Quotation Marks, Double Negatives, Comma (To Set Off Dialogue)**

Yesterday our teacher told us‸*"*Class, some people say that Betsy Ross

didn't ~~never~~ design the American flag; some say Francis Hopkinson did

that.*"*

WEEK 27: Signs and Symbols

■ **Comma (Between Two Independent Clauses), Subject-Verb Agreement, End Punctuation**

School-crossing signs are yellow but what color is hospital signs.

■ **Using the Right Word, Comma (Items in a Series), Verb (Irregular)**

I want my little brother two be safe on his bike, sew I teached him that red means stop yellow means caution and green means go.

■ **Comma (To Set Off Introductory Phrases and Clauses), Hyphen, Using the Right Word**

When people go walking at night they should where reflective material or light colored clothing.

■ **Subject-Verb Agreement, Comma (To Separate Adjectives)**

To help keep them safe on the job, construction workers wears brightly colored hard hats and heavy metal-toed boots.

■ **Subject-Verb Agreement, Using the Right Word**

Wires used buy electricians is color-coded to prevent accidents and fires.

WEEK 27: **Corrected Sentences**

- **Comma (Between Two Independent Clauses), Subject-Verb Agreement, End Punctuation**

  School-crossing signs are yellow, but what color ~~is~~ *are* hospital signs. ?

- **Using the Right Word, Comma (Items in a Series), Verb (Irregular)**

  I want my little brother ~~two~~ *to* be safe on his bike, ~~sew~~ *so* I ~~teached~~ *taught* him that

  red means stop, yellow means caution, and green means go.

- **Comma (To Set Off Introductory Phrases and Clauses), Hyphen, Using the Right Word**

  When people go walking at night, they should ~~where~~ *wear* reflective material or

  light-colored clothing.

- **Subject-Verb Agreement, Comma (To Separate Adjectives)**

  To help keep them safe on the job, construction workers ~~wears~~ *wear* brightly

  colored hard hats and heavy, metal-toed boots.

- **Subject-Verb Agreement, Using the Right Word**

  Wires used ~~buy~~ *by* electricians ~~is~~ *are* color-coded to prevent accidents and fires.

WEEK 28: U.S. History

■ **Using the Right Word, Italics and Underlining, Capitalization**

Thomas Paine helped americans understand the true meaning of freedom by righting The Age of Reason and other books.

■ **Abbreviations, Numbers, Period**

In nineteen ninety, L Douglas Wilder became the first African American elected governor in the U.S.

■ **Comma (To Set Off Introductory Phrases and Clauses), Capitalization, Using the Right Word**

Though you probably no the first president of the united states do you know the first vice president?

■ **Run-On Sentence, Verb (Irregular), Comma (To Keep Numbers Clear), Quotation Marks**

My history teacher said, The first American train robbery taked place in 1866 the robbers made off with $16000.

■ **Comma (To Set Off Appositives), Capitalization, Verb (Irregular)**

George Washington the first president of the united States was sweared into office in New York City.

WEEK 28: **Corrected Sentences**

■ Using the Right Word, Italics and Underlining, Capitalization

Thomas Paine helped *A*mericans understand the true meaning of freedom

by ~~righting~~ *writing* The Age of Reason and other books.

■ Abbreviations, Numbers, Period

In ~~nineteen ninety~~, *1990* L. Douglas Wilder became the first African American

elected governor in the ~~U.S.~~ *United States*

■ Comma (To Set Off Introductory Phrases and Clauses), Capitalization, Using the Right Word

Though you probably ~~no~~ *know* the first president of the *U*nited *S*tates, do you

know the first vice president?

■ Run-On Sentence, Verb (Irregular), Comma (To Keep Numbers Clear), Quotation Marks

My history teacher said, "The first American train robbery ~~taked~~ *took* place in

1866; the robbers made off with $16,000."

■ Comma (To Set Off Appositives), Capitalization, Verb (Irregular)

George Washington, the first president of the *U*nited States, was ~~sweared~~ *sworn*

into office in New York City.

WEEK 29: The Civil War and Before

- ## Using the Right Word, Numbers

  Native Americans lived hear for thousands of years before Columbus "discovered" America in fourteen ninety-two.

- ## Numbers, Comma (In Addresses), Run-On Sentence

  The first Spanish colony in America was established in Pensacola Florida in 1559 it lasted only 2 years.

- ## Comma (Between Two Independent Clauses), Using the Right Word, Capitalization

  The South eventually decided to brake away from the Union and the southern states formed the confederate states of america.

- ## Run-On Sentence, Verb (Irregular)

  General Robert E. Lee leaded the army for the South Ulysses S. Grant becomed the top general for the North.

- ## Capitalization, Comma (In Addresses), Abbreviations

  The confederate states of America established their capital in richmond VA.

WEEK 29: **Corrected Sentences**

■ Using the Right Word, Numbers

Native Americans lived ~~hear~~ *here* for thousands of years before Columbus

"discovered" America in ~~fourteen ninety-two~~ *1492*.

■ Numbers, Comma (In Addresses), Run-On Sentence

The first Spanish colony in America was established in Pensacola, Florida,

in 1559. ⊙t lasted only *two* ~~2~~ years.

■ Comma (Between Two Independent Clauses), Using the Right Word, Capitalization

The South eventually decided to ~~brake~~ *break* away from the Union, and the

southern states formed the *C* ¢onfederate *S* ¢tates of *A* ∤merica.

■ Run-On Sentence, Verb (Irregular)

General Robert E. Lee ~~leaded~~ *led* the army for the South⊙Ulysses S. Grant

became ~~becomed~~ the top general for the North.

■ Capitalization, Comma (In Addresses), Abbreviations

The *C* ¢onfederate *S* ¢tates of America established their capital in *R* ∤ichmond,

Virginia ~~VA~~.

WEEK 30: Science Now and Then

■ **Colon, Numbers, Quotation Marks (Special Words)**

Our science class met at 1030 this morning in the park, and Mr. Bartz

showed us the fifty annual rings on a cross section of a freshly cut tree.

■ **Capitalization, Comma (To Set Off Introductory Phrases and Clauses)**

After five walks in space astronauts were able to repair the hubble

telescope.

■ **Subject-Verb Agreement, Adjective (Comparative/Superlative), Using the Right Word**

The recentest theory says the extinction of dinosaurs were probably

caused by a meteorite who hit the earth.

■ **Numbers, Apostrophe (In Possessives), Verb (Irregular)**

The dinosaurs extinction taked place about 65,000,000 years ago.

■ **Subject-Verb Agreement, Plurals, Double Negatives**

Some peoples still wonder if there never was no dinosaurs.

WEEK 30: **Corrected Sentences**

■ **Colon, Numbers, Quotation Marks (Special Words)**

Our science class met at 10:30 this morning in the park, and Mr. Bartz

showed us the ~~fifty~~ *50* "annual rings" on a cross section of a freshly cut tree.

■ **Capitalization, Comma (To Set Off Introductory Phrases and Clauses)**

After five walks in space, astronauts were able to repair the *H*ubble

telescope.

■ **Subject-Verb Agreement, Adjective (Comparative/Superlative), Using the Right Word**

The ~~recentest~~ *most recent* theory says the extinction of dinosaurs ~~were~~ *was* probably

caused by a meteorite ~~who~~ *that* hit the earth.

■ **Numbers, Apostrophe (In Possessives), Verb (Irregular)**

The dinosaurs' extinction ~~taked~~ *took* place about ~~65,000,000~~ *65 million* years ago.

■ **Subject-Verb Agreement, Plurals, Double Negatives**

Some ~~peoples~~ *people* still wonder if there ~~never was no~~ *ever were any* dinosaurs.

WEEK 31: Science Facts

■ **Capitalization, Hyphen, Apostrophe (In Possessives)**

At certain times during the Ice age, one third of the earths surface was covered with ice.

■ **Comma (In Addresses), Run-On Sentence, Apostrophe (In Possessives)**

Glaciers are large rivers of moving ice I have seen pieces break off at the oceans edge to form icebergs near Juneau Alaska.

■ **Comma (Between Two Independent Clauses), Subject-Verb Agreement, Apostrophe (In Contractions)**

The interior of the earth get hot enough to melt rock and thats how lava are formed.

■ **Numbers, Adjective (Comparative/Superlative)**

The most oldest rock ever found is almost 4,000,000,000 years old!

■ **Comma (Between Two Independent Clauses), Double Subjects, Adverb (Comparative/Superlative)**

The earth it is made of many layers and the heaviest metals lie more closer to the center.

WEEK 31: **Corrected Sentences**

■ **Capitalization, Hyphen, Apostrophe (In Possessives)**

At certain times during the Ice *A*ge, one-third of the earth*'*s surface was

covered with ice.

■ **Comma (In Addresses), Run-On Sentence, Apostrophe (In Possessives)**

Glaciers are large rivers of moving ice. I have seen pieces break off at

the ocean*'*s edge to form icebergs near Juneau, Alaska.

■ **Comma (Between Two Independent Clauses), Subject-Verb Agreement, Apostrophe (In Contractions)**

The interior of the earth ~~get~~ *gets* hot enough to melt rock, and that*'*s how

lava ~~are~~ *is* formed.

■ **Numbers, Adjective (Comparative/Superlative)**

The ~~most~~ oldest rock ever found is almost ~~4,000,000,000~~ *4 billion* years old!

■ **Comma (Between Two Independent Clauses), Double Subjects, Adverb (Comparative/Superlative)**

The earth ~~it~~ is made of many layers, and the heaviest metals lie ~~more~~

closer to the center.

WEEK 32: Inventors and Inventions

■ **Comma (To Set Off Appositives), Using the Right Word, Abbreviations**

Willis Carrier a scientist from NY invented the first heir conditioner.

■ **Hyphen, Comma (To Set Off Appositives and In Addresses)**

The first air conditioned building a movie theater was located in Chicago Illinois.

■ **Using the Right Word, Comma (To Set Off Appositives), Period**

Philo T Farnsworth the father of television invented the electronic device that maid television possible.

■ **Capitalization, Run-On Sentence**

In 1929, Vladimir k. Zworykin invented the first electronic tv system he was a Russian-born american.

■ **Comma (To Set Off Interruptions), Spelling**

The first picture seen on television was beleive it or not Felix the Cat.

WEEK 32: **Corrected Sentences**

- **Comma (To Set Off Appositives), Using the Right Word, Abbreviations**

Willis Carrier, a scientist from ~~NY~~ *New York*, invented the first ~~heir~~ *air* conditioner.

- **Hyphen, Comma (To Set Off Appositives and In Addresses)**

The first air-conditioned building, a movie theater, was located in Chicago, Illinois.

- **Using the Right Word, Comma (To Set Off Appositives), Period**

Philo T. Farnsworth, the father of television, invented the electronic device that ~~maid~~ *made* television possible.

- **Capitalization, Run-On Sentence**

In 1929, Vladimir *K*. Zworykin invented the first electronic *TV* system. *H*e was a Russian-born *A*merican.

- **Comma (To Set Off Interruptions), Spelling**

The first picture seen on television was, *believe* ~~beleive~~ it or not, Felix the Cat.

WEEK 33: Story Time

- **Apostrophe (In Possessives), Comma (To Set Off Interruptions), Using the Right Word**

Sir Gawain in fact ended up being the only night in King Arthurs court who excepted the gigantic Green Knights challenge to battle.

- **Italics and Underlining, Comma (Items in a Series), Sentence Fragment**

Dickens's book A Christmas Carol about greed change and love.

- **Comma (To Set Off Appositives), Sentence Problems ("Of" for "Have"), Italics and Underlining**

You would of liked The Nutcracker the ballet about a girl who dreams of the land of the Sugar Plum Fairy.

- **Quotation Marks, End Punctuation, Pronoun-Antecedent Agreement**

Have you read the fairy tale Beauty and the Beast, or have you only seen them as a movie.

- **Comma (To Set Off Appositives), Capitalization, Plurals**

Agatha Christie a famous writer of mysterys created the first female detective miss Jane Marple.

WEEK 33: **Corrected Sentences**

- ### Apostrophe (In Possessives), Comma (To Set Off Interruptions), Using the Right Word

  Sir Gawain, in fact, ended up being the only ~~night~~ *knight* in King Arthur's court

  who ~~excepted~~ *accepted* the gigantic Green Knight's challenge to battle.

- ### Italics and Underlining, Comma (Items in a Series), Sentence Fragment

  Dickens's book <u>A Christmas Carol</u> *is* about greed, change, and love.

- ### Comma (To Set Off Appositives), Sentence Problems ("Of" for "Have"), Italics and Underlining

  You would ~~of~~ *have* liked <u>The Nutcracker</u>, the ballet about a girl who dreams of

  the land of the Sugar Plum Fairy.

- ### Quotation Marks, End Punctuation, Pronoun-Antecedent Agreement

  Have you read the fairy tale "Beauty and the Beast," or have you only

  seen ~~them~~ *it* as a movie?

- ### Comma (To Set Off Appositives), Capitalization, Plurals

  Agatha Christie, a famous writer of ~~mysterys~~ *mysteries*, created the first female

  detective, *M*iss Jane Marple.

WEEK 34: Literature and Life

- **Comma (To Set Off Introductory Phrases and Clauses), Capitalization, Italics and Underlining**

  In the book charlie and the chocolate factory Charlie finds a winning ticket in a Whipple-Scrumptious Fudgemallow Delight candy bar.

- **Comma (In Addresses), Plurals, Italics and Underlining**

  The book Curious George and all the other storys about this amusing monkey are published by Houghton Mifflin Company 222 Berkeley Street Boston MA 02116.

- **Comma (In Dates), Quotation Marks, Period**

  I said, There are nine rocket candles on my cake, and it's 9 p m on my golden birthday today, September 9 1999!

- **Quotation Marks (Special Words), Using the Right Word**

  Humble is the last word that Charlotte rights in her web.

- **Italics and Underlining, Apostrophe (In Possessives), Capitalization**

  Shel Silversteins first book was Lafcadio: the Lion Who Shot Back.

WEEK 34: **Corrected Sentences**

- **Comma (To Set Off Introductory Phrases and Clauses), Capitalization, Italics and Underlining**

In the book <u>*C*harlie and the *C*hocolate *F*actory</u>, Charlie finds a winning

ticket in a Whipple-Scrumptious Fudgemallow Delight candy bar.

- **Comma (In Addresses), Plurals, Italics and Underlining**

The book <u>Curious George</u> and all the other ~~storys~~ *stories* about this amusing

monkey are published by Houghton Mifflin Company, 222 Berkeley Street,

Boston, MA 02116.

- **Comma (In Dates), Quotation Marks, Period**

I said, "There are nine rocket candles on my cake, and it's 9 p.m. on my

golden birthday today, September 9, 1999!"

- **Quotation Marks (Special Words), Using the Right Word**

"Humble" is the last word that Charlotte ~~rights~~ *writes* in her web.

- **Italics and Underlining, Apostrophe (In Possessives), Capitalization**

Shel Silverstein's first book was <u>Lafcadio: *T*he Lion Who Shot Back</u>.

WEEK 35: Fictional Characters

- **Comma (Between Two Independent Clauses and To Set Off Interruptions)**

George and Martha of course are names of a famous couple in history but they are also the names of two hippo friends in a storybook.

- **Hyphen, Quotation Marks, Comma (Items in a Series)**

A 10 year old Japanese club teaches its members Mother Goose nursery rhymes, such as Little Jack Horner "Little Miss Muffet" and Humpty Dumpty.

- **Apostrophe (In Possessives), Double Subjects, Italics and Underlining**

In Child of the Owl, Caseys Grandmother Paw-Paw she lives in Chinatown.

- **Using the Right Word, Subject-Verb Agreement, Italics and Underlining**

Pippi Longstocking is a book about a spunky girl who can lift a horse and don't where shoes or like school.

- **Comma (To Set Off Introductory Phrases and Clauses), Using the Right Word**

When he needed a brake Sherlock Holmes learned himself to play the violin.

WEEK 35: **Corrected Sentences**

- **Comma (Between Two Independent Clauses and To Set Off Interruptions)**

George and Martha, of course, are names of a famous couple in history, but they are also the names of two hippo friends in a storybook.

- **Hyphen, Quotation Marks, Comma (Items in a Series)**

A 10-year-old Japanese club teaches its members Mother Goose nursery rhymes, such as "Little Jack Horner," "Little Miss Muffet," and "Humpty Dumpty."

- **Apostrophe (In Possessives), Double Subjects, Italics and Underlining**

In <u>Child of the Owl</u>, Casey's Grandmother Paw-Paw ~~she~~ lives in Chinatown.

- **Using the Right Word, Subject-Verb Agreement, Italics and Underlining**

Pippi Longstocking is a book about a spunky girl who can lift a horse and ~~don't where~~ *doesn't wear* shoes or like school.

- **Comma (To Set Off Introductory Phrases and Clauses), Using the Right Word**

When he needed a ~~brake~~, *break* Sherlock Holmes ~~learned~~ *taught* himself to play the violin.

MUG Shot
Paragraphs

The MUG Shot paragraphs are a quick and efficient way to review **m**echanics, **u**sage, and **g**rammar errors each week. These paragraphs can also serve as excellent proofreading exercises. Each paragraph can be corrected and discussed in 8 to 10 minutes.

Implementation and Evaluation

For each set of MUG Shot sentences, there is a corresponding MUG Shot paragraph. The first 18 weeks of MUG Shot paragraphs focus on the one or two skills addressed in each week's sentences. The remaining 17 weeks of paragraphs feature a mixed review of proofreading skills addressing select editing and proofreading skills covered in each week's sentences.

Implementation

A MUG Shot paragraph can be implemented at the end of the week as a review or an evaluation activity. It may be done orally as a class. Otherwise you may simply distribute copies of the week's paragraph, read the paragraph aloud, and then have students make their corrections on the sheet. Students may use the "Editing and Proofreading Marks" in their handbooks or on page iv. Have students then discuss their changes (in pairs or in small groups). Afterward, go over the paragraph as a class to make sure that everyone understands the reasons for the changes. (You may want to refer to the corresponding MUG Shot sentences during your discussion.)

An Alternative Approach: Distribute copies of the MUG Shot paragraph along with the edited version. (They appear on the same page in your booklet.) Have students fold the edited version under, and then make their own changes. Once they are finished, they can unfold the paper and check their work.

Evaluation

If you use the paragraphs as an evaluation activity, we recommend that you give students a basic performance score for their work. This score should reflect the number of changes the student has marked correctly (before or after any discussion). The weekly score might also reflect the student's work on the corresponding MUG Shot sentences.

Note: In the MUG Shot paragraphs showing corrections for run-on sentences, sentence fragments, and sentence combining, one possible correction is shown. However, there are often a number of possible answers that would also be correct.

WEEK 1: California's Name

■ End Punctuation

What state is named after a character in a book In 1535, the Spanish explorer Cortés came to Baja, California He thought it looked like the beautiful island in a story he had read. The female ruler of the island was named Calafia Ten years later, the area was called California Awesome California was named after a powerful Spanish woman

WEEK 1: **Corrected Paragraph**

What state is named after a character in a book ? In 1535, the Spanish explorer Cortés came to Baja, California. He thought it looked like the beautiful island in a story he had read. The female ruler of the island was named Calafia. Ten years later, the area was called California. Awesome ! California was named after a powerful Spanish woman. (or) !

WEEK 2: If You're an Anteater

■ Comma (Items in a Series)

Anteaters live in Mexico Honduras Panama and other places. They have long heads long tongues and no teeth. Woods swamps and plains are their homes. They eat ants termites and other insects. Their front claws tear open anthills. Then they stick their long tongues into the ant hills lick up the insects and eat them. If you're an anteater, you don't mind eating insects for breakfast lunch and dinner.

WEEK 2: **Corrected Paragraph**

Anteaters live in Mexico, Honduras, Panama, and other places. They have long heads, long tongues, and no teeth. Woods, swamps, and plains are their homes. They eat ants, termites, and other insects. Their front claws tear open anthills. Then they stick their long tongues into the ant hills, lick up the insects, and eat them. If you're an anteater, you don't mind eating insects for breakfast, lunch, and dinner.

WEEK 3: Happy Birthday, U.S.A.

■ Comma (In Dates and In Addresses)

Independence Day was first celebrated on July 8 1776. The Declaration of Independence was read out loud in Philadelphia Pennsylvania. Church bells rang, people cheered, and bands played. On July 4 1941 the Fourth of July became an official United States holiday. Many people celebrate the Fourth with parades, picnics, and fireworks. All my relatives gather at 101 Center Street Lakewood Iowa every year for a great family picnic. We have a sack race, an egg toss, and some volleyball games.

WEEK 3: **Corrected Paragraph**

Independence Day was first celebrated on July 8, 1776. The Declaration of Independence was read out loud in Philadelphia, Pennsylvania. Church bells rang, people cheered, and bands played. On July 4, 1941, the Fourth of July became an official United States holiday. Many people celebrate the Fourth with parades, picnics, and fireworks. All my relatives gather at 101 Center Street, Lakewood, Iowa, every year for a great family picnic. We have a sack race, an egg toss, and some volleyball games.

WEEK 4: Rain, Rain, Go Away

■ Comma (To Keep Numbers Clear and to Set Off Interjections)

Who gets the most rain? Well in the United States it's the Southeast. Some places there get around 1778 millimeters a year (that's 70 inches). The average yearly rainfall in northeastern India is 10922 millimeters (that's about 430 inches). Wow the Philippines holds the record for the most rain in one day. During a typhoon, they got nearly 1168 millimeters (almost 46 inches)!

WEEK 4: **Corrected Paragraph**

Who gets the most rain? Well, in the United States it's the Southeast. Some places there get around 1,778 millimeters a year (that's 70 inches). The average yearly rainfall in northeastern India is 10,922 millimeters (that's about 430 inches). Wow, the Philippines holds the record for the most rain in one day. During a typhoon, they got nearly 1,168 millimeters (almost 46 inches)!

WEEK 5: Mt. McKinley First

■ **Comma (Between Two Independent Clauses)**

The highest mountain in North America is Mt. McKinley in Alaska but its Native American name is *Denali*. The word *Denali* means "High One" and it is. Mt. McKinley is 20,320 feet high. Rev. Hudson Stuck led a four-man team to the top in 1913. Walter Harper, a Native American from Alaska, got there first but the others were right behind him. The men thanked God and they planted a cross of sticks.

WEEK 5: **Corrected Paragraph**

The highest mountain in North America is Mt. McKinley in Alaska, but its Native American name is *Denali*. The word *Denali* means "High One," and it is. Mt. McKinley is 20,320 feet high. Rev. Hudson Stuck led a four-man team to the top in 1913. Walter Harper, a Native American from Alaska, got there first, but the others were right behind him. The men thanked God, and they planted a cross of sticks.

WEEK 6: Football Fans

■ **Hyphen**

While one half of our family stays home, my dad and I zip off to the football game. In our town, most games have sellout crowds. We arrive two hours early to find an on site parking space. We wave to fun loving fans. Then we climb to our upper deck seats. The bone chilling wind whips around us in our nosebleed seats. We don't care. We are "all American" football fans!

WEEK 6: Corrected Paragraph

While one-half of our family stays home, my dad and I zip off to the football game. In our town, most games have sellout crowds. We arrive two hours early to find an on-site parking space. We wave to fun-loving fans. Then we climb to our upper-deck seats. The bone-chilling wind whips around us in our nosebleed seats. We don't care. We are "all-American" football fans!

WEEK 7: Good Books

■ Apostrophe (In Contractions and In Possessives)

Have you ever read a book that you couldnt put down? Two popular childrens books are *Charlottes Web* and *Dear Mr. Henshaw*. Theyre not new books, but theyre both best-sellers. Kids havent stopped reading them. With these books, maybe youll laugh or maybe youll cry. Youll feel and think about what youve read. Thats one reason why some books dont get dusty.

WEEK 7: Corrected Paragraph

Have you ever read a book that you couldn't put down? Two popular children's books are *Charlotte's Web* and *Dear Mr. Henshaw*. They're not new books, but they're both best-sellers. Kids haven't stopped reading them. With these books, maybe you'll laugh or maybe you'll cry. You'll feel and think about what you've read. That's one reason why some books don't get dusty.

WEEK 8: Girl with the Crooked Hair

■ Quotation Marks

Writer Sandra Cisneros wrote a short story called Eleven. She said, When I think how I see myself, I would have to be at age 11. I know I'm 32 on the outside, but inside I'm 11. When she was young, her family traveled between Chicago and Mexico. I didn't like school because we moved so much, she said. Another problem was her looks. She said, I'm the girl in the picture with skinny arms and a crumpled shirt and crooked hair. Today, Cisneros is a well-known writer.

•

WEEK 8: **Corrected Paragraph**

Writer Sandra Cisneros wrote a short story called "Eleven." She said, "When I think how I see myself, I would have to be at age 11. I know I'm 32 on the outside, but inside I'm 11." When she was young, her family traveled between Chicago and Mexico. "I didn't like school because we moved so much," she said. Another problem was her looks. She said, "I'm the girl in the picture with skinny arms and a crumpled shirt and crooked hair." Today, Cisneros is a well-known writer.

WEEK 9: The Real McCoy

■ Capitalization

Elijah McCoy was born before the civil war ended. his mother and father were ex-slaves. they escaped to canada on the underground railroad. later they returned to the united states. their son, elijah, went to scotland to study Engineering. when he returned, no one would hire an african american engineer. in spite of that, Elijah McCoy became a famous inventor. when people wanted a particular invention of McCoy's, they asked for the "real McCoy."

WEEK 9: **Corrected Paragraph**

Elijah McCoy was born before the *C*ivil *W*ar ended. *H*is mother and father were ex-slaves. *T*hey escaped to *C*anada on the *U*nderground *R*ailroad. *L*ater they returned to the *U*nited *S*tates. *T*heir son, *E*lijah, went to *S*cotland to study *E*ngineering. *W*hen he returned, no one would hire an *A*frican *A*merican engineer. *I*n spite of that, Elijah McCoy became a famous inventor. *W*hen people wanted a particular invention of McCoy's, they asked for the "real McCoy."

WEEK 10: The Perfect Vacation

■ Capitalization

For a perfect vacation, would you go west to the rockies or east to the appalachian mountains? how about kicking around in the atlantic ocean or the gulf of mexico? Do you dream of going to yellowstone national park, niagara falls, or the grand canyon? How about a trip to europe or africa? If you want to fly to the Moon, you'll have to wait a few years.

WEEK 10: **Corrected Paragraph**

For a perfect vacation, would you go west to the R̸ockies or east to the A̸ppalachian M̸ountains? H̸ow about kicking around in the A̸tlantic O̸cean or the G̸ulf of M̸exico? Do you dream of going to Y̸ellowstone N̸ational P̸ark, N̸iagara F̸alls, or the G̸rand C̸anyon? How about a trip to E̸urope or A̸frica? If you want to fly to the m̸oon, you'll have to wait a few years.

WEEK 11: Looking at Art

■ Plurals

The buses dropped us off at the art museum. Four bronze horsemans guarded the entrance. They had swords and knifes. Angeles with halos were painted on the ceiling. Our guide led us through rooms called gallerys. Paintings of tables piled with food started making us hungry. Later, we ate box lunchs. Inside were sandwichs or tacos, a couple spoonsful of fruit salad, and big chocolate-chip cookys shaped like leafs.

WEEK 11: Corrected Paragraph

The buses dropped off us at the art museum. Four bronze ~~horsemans~~ *horsemen* guarded the entrance. They had swords and ~~knifes~~ *knives*. ~~Angeles~~ *Angels* with halos were painted on the ceiling. Our guide led us through rooms called ~~gallerys~~ *galleries*. Paintings of tables piled with food started making us hungry. Later, we ate box ~~lunchs~~ *lunches*. Inside were ~~sandwichs~~ *sandwiches* or tacos, a couple ~~spoonsful~~ *spoonfuls* of fruit salad, and big chocolate-chip ~~cookys~~ *cookies* shaped like ~~leafs~~ *leaves*.

WEEK 12: The First Americans

■ Numbers

20,000 years ago, the first people probably wandered into North and South America from northeast Asia. Nearly 1,000,000 Native Americans were living in the United States when Columbus "discovered" them. By nineteen ten, wars, sickness, and starvation left only 220 thousand Native Americans. 2,000,000 Native Americans live in the United States today. They are not 1 people, but many different peoples with their own histories and ways of life.

WEEK 12: **Corrected Paragraph**

Twenty thousand
~~20,000~~ years ago, the first people probably wandered into North and
1 million
South America from northeast Asia. Nearly ~~1,000,000~~ Native Americans

were living in the United States when Columbus "discovered" them. By
1910   *220,000*
~~nineteen ten~~, wars, sickness, and starvation left only ~~220 thousand~~ Native
Two million
Americans. ~~2,000,000~~ Native Americans live in the United States today.
one
They are not ~~1~~ people, but many different peoples with their own

histories and ways of life.

WEEK 13: Tornado Watch

■ Subject-Verb Agreement

What causes a tornado? A "front" form between a cold air mass and a warm air mass. Sometimes a cold air mass move in above the warm air. The hot air rises. It spins. Then it form a funnel-shaped cloud—a tornado. Weather experts looks for these conditions. Then they gives a "tornado watch." The winds inside a tornado may reach 500 miles per hour. Sometimes a tornado touch the ground and destroy everything in its way.

WEEK 13: Corrected Paragraph

What causes a tornado? A "front" ~~form~~ *forms* between a cold air mass and a warm air mass. Sometimes a cold air mass ~~move~~ *moves* in above the warm air. The hot air rises. It spins. Then it ~~form~~ *forms* a funnel-shaped cloud—a tornado. Weather experts ~~looks~~ *look* for these conditions. Then they ~~gives~~ *give* a "tornado watch." The winds inside a tornado may reach 500 miles per hour. Sometimes a tornado ~~touch~~ *touches* the ground and ~~destroy~~ *destroys* everything in its way.

WEEK 14: "Oh, Give Me a Home . . . "

■ Subject-Verb Agreement

Where does the deer and the antelope play? One place is Yellowstone National Park. It were created in 1872. Parts of the park is in Wyoming, Montana, and Idaho. The park are a safe place for many animals. Bears, moose, buffalo, deer, and antelope lives there. Beavers, otters, fish, and eagles also enjoys the park. For them, Yellowstone be "home sweet home."

WEEK 14: **Corrected Paragraph**

Where ~~does~~ *do* the deer and the antelope play? One place is Yellowstone National Park. It ~~were~~ *was* created in 1872. Parts of the park ~~is~~ *are* in Wyoming, Montana, and Idaho. The park ~~are~~ *is* a safe place for many animals. Bears, moose, buffalo, deer, and antelope ~~lives~~ *live* there. Beavers, otters, fish, and eagles also ~~enjoys~~ *enjoy* the park. For them, Yellowstone ~~be~~ *is* "home sweet home."

WEEK 15: Dingdong! Crack!

■ Run-On Sentence

Have you ever seen the Liberty Bell it's big, it's old, and it's cracked. The Liberty Bell weighs 2,000 pounds it was around when the United States was still a baby. It rang out to signal holidays, meetings, and fire alarms. It cracked the first time it was used then it was fixed. Many years later, it cracked again this time it could not be fixed. The old bell is on display near Independence Hall in Philadelphia it no longer rings, but it's still the bell of freedom.

WEEK 15: **Corrected Paragraph**

Have you ever seen the Liberty Bell? It's big, it's old, and it's cracked. The Liberty Bell weighs 2,000 pounds. It was around when the United States was still a baby. It rang out to signal holidays, meetings, and fire alarms. It cracked the first time it was used. Then it was fixed. Many years later, it cracked again. This time it could not be fixed. The old bell is on display near Independence Hall in Philadelphia. It no longer rings, but it's still the bell of freedom.

WEEK 16: Everybody Has Rights

■ Sentence Fragment

Dorothea Dix. Born in Maine in 1802. She taught school for many years. Then volunteered to teach a Sunday school class in a prison. What she found was shocking. Mental patients. Shared prison cells with criminals and were treated worse than animals. Wrote a long report. Mental patients not being criminals. Many things changed because of Dorothea Dix.

WEEK 16: **Corrected Paragraph**

Dorothea Dix *was* Born in Maine in 1802. She taught school for many years. Then *she* volunteered to teach a Sunday school class in a prison. What she found was shocking. Mental patients *s* Shared prison cells with criminals and were treated worse than animals. *Dorothea w* Wrote a long report *about* *m* Mental patients not being criminals. Many things changed because of Dorothea Dix.

WEEK 17: Hey, Pick That Up!

■ Using the Right Word

Does it matter what you do with you're trash? Yes, it does! You no how you run out of things at home. Earth could run out of things, to. It could run out of clean air and fresh water. But there are alot of ways to help. Sit up a recycling program at your school, or right an article four your school paper. Bring bottles, newspapers, and aluminum cans to a recycling center. Learn others what to do. You *can* have a positive affect.

WEEK 17: Corrected Paragraph

Does it matter what you do with ~~you're~~ *your* trash? Yes, it does! You ~~no~~ *know* how you run out of things at home. Earth could run out of things, ~~to~~ *too*. It could run out of clean air and fresh water. But there are ~~alot~~ *a lot* of ways to help. ~~Sit~~ *Set* up a recycling program at your school, or ~~right~~ *write* an article ~~four~~ *for* your school paper. ~~Bring~~ *Take* bottles, newspapers, and aluminum cans to a recycling center. ~~Learn~~ *Teach* others what to do. You *can* have a positive ~~affect~~ *effect*.

WEEK 18: The Nearest Planet

■ Combining Sentences

Did you ever look for Venus in the sky? Did you ever look for Venus in the evening? Venus is a planet. Venus is a bright planet. It is between Earth and Mercury. It reflects the sun's light. It has no light of its own. Its environment is red-hot. Its environment would burn you to a crisp if you were there. Venus has pools of liquid metal. Venus has clouds of liquid acid. It has lightning storms. It has erupting volcanoes.

WEEK 18: **Corrected Paragraph**

Did you ever look for Venus in the ∧*evening* sky? ~~Did you ever look for Venus in the evening?~~ Venus is a ∧*bright* planet. ~~Venus is a bright planet. It is~~ between Earth and Mercury. It reflects the sun's light, ∧*but* ~~It~~ has no light of its own. Its ∧*red-hot* environment ~~is red-hot. Its environment~~ would burn you to a crisp if you were there. Venus has pools of liquid metal, ∧*and* ~~Venus has~~ clouds of liquid acid. It has lightning storms, ∧*and* ~~It has~~ erupting volcanoes.

WEEK 19: Fingers Do the Talking

■ Sentence Problems ("Of" for "Have"), Verb (Irregular), Run-On Sentence

The Plains Indians of North America belonged to many different tribes they speaked many different languages. How could they communicate? They used their hands to make signs for creeks, rivers, and fir trees. White men wore hats the sign for a white man showed a hat. Some signs had several meanings. If an Indian pretended to shiver, that could of meant cold it could also of meant winter weather. Sign language is a creative way of talking.

WEEK 19: Corrected Paragraph

The Plains Indians of North America belonged to many different
T   spoke
tribes. They ~~speaked~~ many different languages. How could they
communicate? They used their hands to make signs for creeks, rivers,
                                    so
and fir trees. White men wore hats, the sign for a white man showed a
hat. Some signs had several meanings. If an Indian pretended to shiver,
            have   I   have
that could ~~of~~ meant cold. It could also ~~of~~ meant winter weather. Sign
language is a creative way of talking.

WEEK 20: Spelling Challenge

■ **Comma (Items in a Series), Pronoun-Antecedent Agreement,
Subject-Verb Agreement, Capitalization**

Where is English spoken? The countries includes the United States,
the United kingdom, Canada, Australia new Zealand and south africa.
English have the largest vocabulary in the world. It has "borrowed"
words from European, Arabic African and asian languages. Many English
words are hard to spell. It is often not spelled the way it sounds (*night,*
through, and *reign*).

WEEK 20: **Corrected Paragraph**

Where is English spoken? The countries ~~includes~~ *include* the United States,
the United ~~k~~*K*ingdom, Canada, Australia*,* *N*new Zealand*,* and *S*south *A*africa.
English ~~have~~ *has* the largest vocabulary in the world. It has "borrowed"
words from European, Arabic*,* African*,* and *A*asian languages. Many English
words are hard to spell. ~~It is~~ *They are* often not spelled the way ~~it sounds~~ *they sound* (*night,*
through, and *reign*).

WEEK 21: Fishy Facts

■ Adjective (Comparative/Superlative), Pronoun-Antecedent Agreement, Comma (To Set Off Interjections), Numbers, Semicolon

The following facts might sound fishy to you, but it's true. Atlantic salmon can leap fifteen feet into the air. Yes but that's a small distance compared to flying fish. They don't actually fly they glide through the air. They can travel more than ninety feet if they're being chased. The most fast fish of all is the sailfish. It has been clocked at sixty miles per hour. Say that's fast enough to get a speeding ticket.

WEEK 21: **Corrected Paragraph**

The following facts might sound fishy to you, but ~~it's~~ *they're* true. Atlantic salmon can leap ~~fifteen~~ *15* feet into the air. Yes*,* but that's a small distance compared to flying fish. They don't actually fly*;* they glide through the air. They can travel more than ~~ninety~~ *90* feet if they're being chased. The ~~most fast~~ *fastest* fish of all is the sailfish. It has been clocked at ~~sixty~~ *60* miles per hour. Say*,* that's fast enough to get a speeding ticket.

WEEK 22: Good Dog

■ **Comma (Items in a Series), Hyphen, Rambling Sentence, Colon**

The poodle is a popular breed of dog in the United States and poodles tend to be intelligent and they are good with kids. Some of the following dogs make good pets golden retrievers Labradors and collies. They are all friendly playful and good natured dogs. You should talk to your dog walk your dog and teach your dog to lie down. If you treat your dog well, you will have a friend for life.

WEEK 22: **Corrected Paragraph**

The poodle is a popular breed of dog in the United States. and
P
poodles tend to be intelligent, and they are good with kids. Some of the following dogs make good pets: golden retrievers, Labradors, and collies. They are all friendly, playful, and good-natured dogs. You should talk to your dog, walk your dog, and teach your dog to lie down. If you treat your dog well, you will have a friend for life.

WEEK 23: The Gulf Stream

■ Comma (In Direct Address), Capitalization, Apostrophe (In Contractions), Spelling

"Students on a map of the United States, you will see a 'finger' in the southeast. Thats the peninsula called florida. It separates the gulf of mexico from the atlantic ocean. The Gulf Stream, a powerful, warm-water current, moves like a river within the ocean. it flows northeast arround Florida. Find the united kingdom on a world map. It has a higher latitude than Maine, but its much warmer. the Gulf Stream warms it up."

WEEK 23: **Corrected Paragraph**

"Students, on a map of the United States, you will see a 'finger' in the Southeast. That's the peninsula called Florida. It separates the Gulf of Mexico from the Atlantic Ocean. The Gulf Stream, a powerful, warm-water current, moves like a river within the ocean. It flows northeast around Florida. Find the United Kingdom on a world map. It has a higher latitude than Maine, but it's much warmer. The Gulf Stream warms it up."

WEEK 24: Look at Minnesota

■ Italics and Underlining, Comma (To Keep Numbers Clear), Double Subjects

About 50000 of Minnesota's 4657758 people are Native Americans. The name of the state comes from a Sioux word. It means "many-tinted waters." Two famous Minnesotans are Judy Garland and Charles Lindbergh. They took trips everyone remembers, but they didn't start from their home state. Judy Garland as Dorothy she traveled from Kansas to Oz in the movie The Wizard of Oz. Charles Lindbergh he flew the first solo airplane flight from New York to Paris in 1927.

WEEK 24: **Corrected Paragraph**

About 50,000 of Minnesota's 4,657,758 people are Native Americans. The name of the state comes from a Sioux word. It means "many-tinted waters." Two famous Minnesotans are Judy Garland and Charles Lindbergh. They took trips everyone remembers, but they didn't start from their home state. Judy Garland as Dorothy ~~she~~ traveled from Kansas to Oz in the movie The Wizard of Oz. Charles Lindbergh ~~he~~ flew the first solo airplane flight from New York to Paris in 1927.

WEEK 25: Hot Spots

- ### Capitalization, Comma (To Separate Adjectives), Using the Right Word, Semicolon

Although a dessert may be hot or cold, it is always dry. Deserts cover about one-fifth of the earth. The biggest desert in north america is the sonoran desert. Death valley is alot smaller it is scarier. It is the hottest driest place in north America. The gold miners in 1849 past through Death Valley. They were unprepared. Many didn't have enough food or water, and so many hungry thirsty miners dyed in that desert.

WEEK 25: Corrected Paragraph

desert
Although a ~~dessert~~ may be hot or cold, it is always dry. Deserts
 N A
cover about one-fifth of the earth. The biggest desert in ɴorth ᴀmerica is
 S D V *a lot*
the ꜱonoran ᴅesert. Death ᴠalley is ~~alot~~ smaller⌃; it is scarier. It is the
 N *passed*
hottest⌃, driest place in ɴorth America. The gold miners in 1849 ~~past~~
through Death Valley. They were unprepared. Many didn't have enough
 died
food or water, and so many hungry⌃, thirsty miners ~~dyed~~ in that desert.

WEEK 26: Don't Step on Me

- ## Quotation Marks, Sentence Fragment, Comma (To Set Off Dialogue), Using the Right Word

One early American flag a rattlesnake printed on it. The flag had this motto "Don't tread on me. That's another way of saying "Don't step on me. When the 13 colonies became the United States. They made a new flag. It had 13 stripes. And 13 stars in a circle. That worked good until knew states came on the seen. Then it was decided to add a new star four every new state. The last pare of stars was added in 1959 for Alaska and Hawaii.

WEEK 26: **Corrected Paragraph**

One early American flag ^had^ a rattlesnake printed on it. The flag had this motto ,^"Don't tread on me.^"^ That's another way of saying ,^"Don't step on me.^"^ When the 13 colonies became the United States ,^ ^t^hey made a new flag. It had 13 stripes ,^ ^a^nd 13 stars in a circle. That worked ~~good~~ ^well^ until ~~knew~~ ^new^ states came on the ~~seen~~ ^scene^. Then it was decided to add a new star ~~four~~ ^for^ every new state. The last ~~pare~~ ^pair^ of stars was added in 1959 for Alaska and Hawaii.

WEEK 27: Safety Engineers

■ **Comma (To Separate Adjectives), Verb (Irregular), End Punctuation**

You have probably heared the saying, "An ounce of prevention is worth a pound of cure." Did you know that there are safety engineers who figure out what can go wrong. They look at things like machines, factories, and roads. Does a machine have a sharp uncovered moving part. Workers could get hurt. Is there a super-sharp turn drivers could run off the road. Safety engineers work on ways to avoid accidents

WEEK 27: **Corrected Paragraph**

You have probably ~~heared~~ *heared* the saying, "An ounce of prevention is worth a pound of cure." Did you know that there are safety engineers who figure out what can go wrong. They look at things like machines, factories, and roads. Does a machine have a sharp, uncovered, moving part. Workers could get hurt. Is there a super-sharp turn, drivers could run off the road. Safety engineers work on ways to avoid accidents.

WEEK 28: Powerful Words

■ **Comma (To Keep Numbers Clear and To Set Off Introductory Phrases and Clauses), Quotation Marks, Italics and Underlining**

Born in England in 1737 Thomas Paine eventually came to America as an adult and then started to write about freedom. He published a little book called Common Sense. It sold more than 500000 copies. The birthday of a new world is at hand, Paine said. A general named George Washington read Paine's words to the troops at Trenton. After hearing the reading the soldiers were inspired, attacked the British, and won. It was a turning point in the Revolutionary War.

WEEK 28: **Corrected Paragraph**

Born in England in 1737, Thomas Paine eventually came to America as an adult and then started to write about freedom. He published a little book called <u>Common Sense</u>. It sold more than 500,000 copies. "The birthday of a new world is at hand," Paine said. A general named George Washington read Paine's words to the troops at Trenton. After hearing the reading, the soldiers were inspired, attacked the British, and won. It was a turning point in the Revolutionary War.

WEEK 29: Flags over Florida

■ **Comma (Between Two Independent Clauses), Capitalization, Numbers, Verb (Irregular)**

In 1698, Spain had a colony in pensacola, florida. In 1719, the french fighted and pushed out the spanish for 3 years. Then the Spanish took over again. Next came the british in 1763. They ruled for twenty years but then the Spanish took over again. Britain controlled pensacola during the war of 1812. In 1814, Pensacola was captured by United States forces. Then Spain recaptured the city for 1 last time. Finally, florida became a state in 1821 and Pensacola became part of the United States.

WEEK 29: Corrected Paragraph

In 1698, Spain had a colony in ~~p~~ensacola, *P* ~~f~~lorida. *F* In 1719, the ~~f~~rench *F*
fought
~~fighted~~ and pushed out the ~~s~~panish *S* for ~~3~~ *three* years. Then the Spanish took
over again. Next came the ~~b~~ritish *B* in 1763. They ruled for ~~twenty~~ *20* years /,\
but then the Spanish took over again. Britain controlled ~~p~~ensacola *P* during
the *W* ~~w~~ar of 1812. In 1814, Pensacola was captured by United States forces.
Then Spain recaptured the city for ~~1~~ *one* last time. Finally, ~~f~~lorida *F* became a
state in 1821 /,\ and Pensacola became part of the United States.

WEEK 30: When Dinosaurs Ruled

- ## Quotation Marks (Special Words), Adjective (Comparative/Superlative), Plurals, Double Negatives

The word *dinosaur* means "terrible lizard. Dinosaurs weren't never really lizards. And they weren't really terrible. Many dinosaurs had big bodies and small brains. Some dinosaurs were plant eaters, and some were meat eaters. One of the most large plant eaters was Seismosaurus (131 feets long). The biggest meat eater was Giganotosaurus (49 feets long). Dinosaurs ruled the earth for 100 million years and then disappeared.

WEEK 30: Corrected Paragraph

The word *dinosaur* means "terrible lizard." Dinosaurs weren't ~~never~~

really lizards. And they weren't really terrible. Many dinosaurs had big

bodies
~~bodys~~ and small brains. Some dinosaurs were plant eaters, and some

largest
were meat eaters. One of the ~~most large~~ plant eaters was Seismosaurus

feet   *feet*
(131 ~~feets~~ long). The biggest meat eater was Giganotosaurus (49 ~~feets~~

long). Dinosaurs ruled the earth for 100 million years and then

disappeared.

WEEK 31: Deep Space

- ### Capitalization, Comma (In Addresses), Run-On Sentence, Adverb (Comparative/Superlative)

People once thought that earth was the center of the universe. Now we know more better. Once we believed our galaxy was the only one in the universe we were wrong about that, too. A galaxy is a collection of stars, planets, and space dust. Our galaxy is called the milky way there are billions of galaxies. In the 1920s, Edwin Hubble, an american astronomer, proved that. The hubble telescope in Palomar California is named after him.

WEEK 31: Corrected Paragraph

People once thought that *E*arth was the center of the universe. Now we know ~~more~~ better. Once we believed our galaxy was the only one in the universe, *but* we were wrong about that, too. A galaxy is a collection of stars, planets, and space dust. Our galaxy is called the *M*ilky *W*ay. *T*here are billions of galaxies. In the 1920s, Edwin Hubble, an *A*merican astronomer, proved that. The *H*ubble telescope in Palomar, California, is named after him.

WEEK 32: Watch the Best, Shut Off the Rest

■ **Comma (To Set Off Appositives and Interruptions), Abbreviations, Run-On Sentence, Hyphen**

Some families have television viewing rules some parents let their kids watch only public television and kids' shows. Some keep the television turned off on school nights. There's junk on tv however there's good stuff, too. Cooking and drawing shows for example teach you something. Other shows field trip or interview programs answer questions about everything from movie special effects to life on aircraft carriers. Parents and kids can make well informed choices.

WEEK 32: **Corrected Paragraph**

Some families have television-viewing rules. Some parents let their kids watch only public television and kids' shows. Some keep the television turned off on school nights. There's junk on TV; however, there's good stuff, too. Cooking and drawing shows, for example, teach you something. Other shows, field trip or interview programs, answer questions about everything from movie special effects to life on aircraft carriers. Parents and kids can make well-informed choices.

WEEK 33: A King from Camelot

■ **Pronoun-Antecedent Agreement, Comma (To Set Off Interruptions), Plurals, End Punctuation**

Do you like tales of knights in shining armor. Do you love beautiful ladys-in-waiting. If you said yes and hopefully you did you'll enjoy *The Legend of King Arthur.* A legend is partly true and partly made up. There probably was a British leader long ago named Arthur. We don't know much about them. We do however have storys about the *legendary* King Arthur and his reign in a kingdom called Camelot

WEEK 33: Corrected Paragraph

Do you like tales of knights in shining armor? Do you love beautiful ladies-in-waiting? If you said yes, and hopefully you did, you'll enjoy *The Legend of King Arthur.* A legend is partly true and partly made up. There probably was a British leader long ago named Arthur. We don't know much about him. We do, however, have stories about the *legendary* King Arthur and his reign in a kingdom called Camelot.

WEEK 34: He Let His Light Shine

- ## Comma (In Dates and In Addresses), Quotation Marks, Plurals, Period, Italics and Underlining

This is how the writer Shel Silverstein described his childhood: "I couldn't play ball, I couldn't dance, luckily, the girls didn't want me, so I started to draw and to write. His first hit was the book The Giving Tree. He also wrote Where the Sidewalk Ends. His books have sold more than 14 million copys. Mr Silverstein died on May 10 1999 in Key West Florida. The world has lost a wonderful writer.

WEEK 34: **Corrected Paragraph**

This is how the writer Shel Silverstein described his childhood: "I couldn't play ball, I couldn't dance, luckily, the girls didn't want me, so I started to draw and to write." His first hit was the book <u>The Giving Tree</u>. He also wrote <u>Where the Sidewalk Ends</u>. His books have sold more than 14 million ~~copys~~ *copies*. Mr. Silverstein died on May 10, 1999, in Key West, Florida. The world has lost a wonderful writer.

WEEK 35: Mother Goose in Japan

■ **Quotation Marks, Subject-Verb Agreement, Comma (Items in a Series), Double Subjects**

Can you recite Mary Had a Little Lamb? Mother Goose rhymes is not just for kids. They're great for people learning English, too. Yasui Sadao he is a high-school English teacher in Japan. He uses Mother Goose poems to teach his students English. Japan it even has a Mother Goose Society. The society has its own Web site newsletter study group and yearly national meeting.

WEEK 35: Corrected Paragraph

Can you recite "Mary Had a Little Lamb"? Mother Goose rhymes ~~is~~ *are* not just for kids. They're great for people learning English, too. Yasui Sadao ~~he~~ is a high-school English teacher in Japan. He uses Mother Goose poems to teach his students English. Japan ~~it~~ even has a Mother Goose Society. The society has its own Web site, newsletter, study group, and yearly national meeting.

Daily Writing Practice

This section offers three types of writing practice. The freewriting done in response to the **writing prompts** can be shared in follow-up sessions and later shaped into finished narratives or essays. The discussion of daily journal writing introduces lists of **writing topics.** The topics address a wide range of writing ideas. Finally "showing" in writing, developed by expanding on the **Show-Me sentences,** can be shared in follow-up sessions and later shaped into finished descriptive paragraphs.

Writing Prompts
A Writing Prompts FAQ Sheet

You may duplicate the following question-and-answer information about writing prompts as a handout for students or use it as the basis for a class discussion.

Anyone who wants to be a good writer has to practice often. That's why so many writers keep journals and diaries. And that's why your teacher asks you to write something nearly every day in school. Your teacher may ask you to write about a specific topic or about a personal experience. Your teacher might also ask you to use a writing prompt.

A writing prompt can be anything from a question to a photograph to a quotation. The idea is for you to write whatever you can without planning or researching the topic. You simply write what you have inside. And you keep writing until all your thoughts are gone. That's it!

How do I get started? It's really very simple. You just write down whatever comes into your mind when you think about your writing prompt. This doesn't have to be much. All you are looking for is an idea to get you going.

Shouldn't I plan out what I'm going to write about? No, you shouldn't plan anything. That's the whole idea. Just write. You don't need to know where your writing will take you. Mystery is good; in fact, it is the mystery and surprises along the way that get writers hooked on writing.

What can I do to keep my writing going? Don't stop! When you run out of ideas, shift gears and try writing about your topic in a slightly different way. For example, you might compare your topic to something else. Or you might use dialogue between two or more people who are discussing your topic. Or you might think of a specific audience—like a group of first graders—and write so they can understand your topic. Whatever you do, keep the ideas flowing as freely as possible.

When should I stop? If you are doing a timed writing (3, 5, or 10 minutes), stop when the time is up. You might decide it's time to stop when you've filled up the entire page. (Or you might keep going, using another sheet of paper.) Or you might decide to stop when you feel that you've done as much thinking and writing as you can and your brain is drained.

What do I do with my writing? You might share it with a classmate and see what she or he thinks. Or you might turn your writing into a more polished essay, story, or poem. Or you might set it aside and use it later when you need a topic for a writing assignment.

So, really, all I have to do is start writing? Right!

WRITING PROMPT

I want to learn to play the . . .

_____

_____

_____

_____

_____

_____

_____

_____

_____

_____

_____

_____

_____

_____

WRITING PROMPT
Life in the Sea

WRITING PROMPT

The tiger was staring right at me.

WRITING PROMPT

In the Middle of the Park

_____

_____

_____

_____

_____

_____

_____

_____

_____

_____

_____

_____

_____

_____

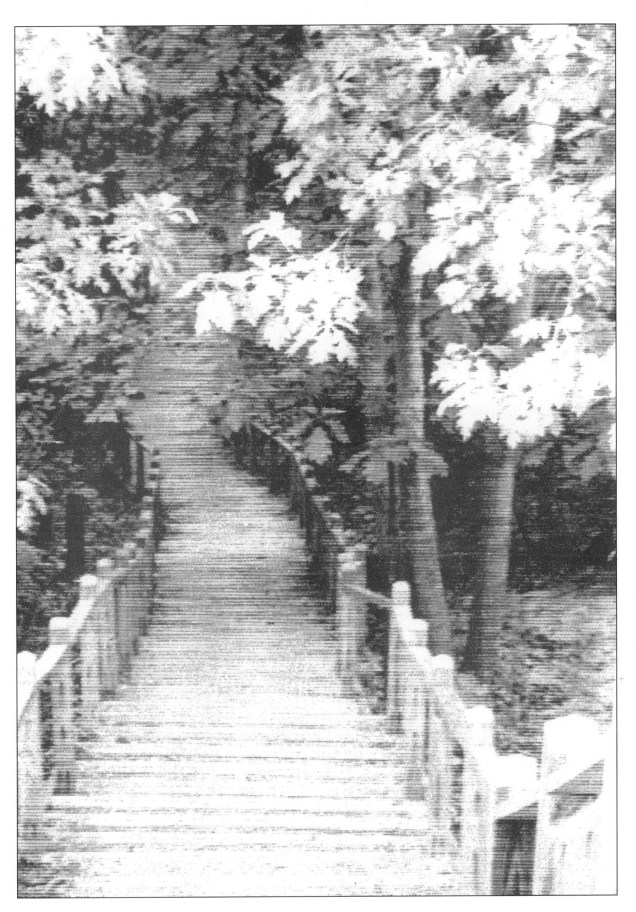

WRITING PROMPT

One little banana peel on the floor was all it took . . .

_____

_____

_____

_____

_____

_____

_____

_____

_____

_____

_____

WRITING PROMPT

Someplace I'd really like to visit . . .

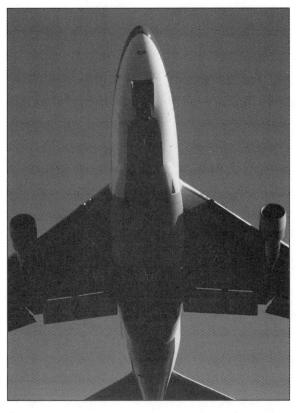

_____

_____

_____

_____

_____

_____

_____

_____

_____

_____

_____

_____

_____

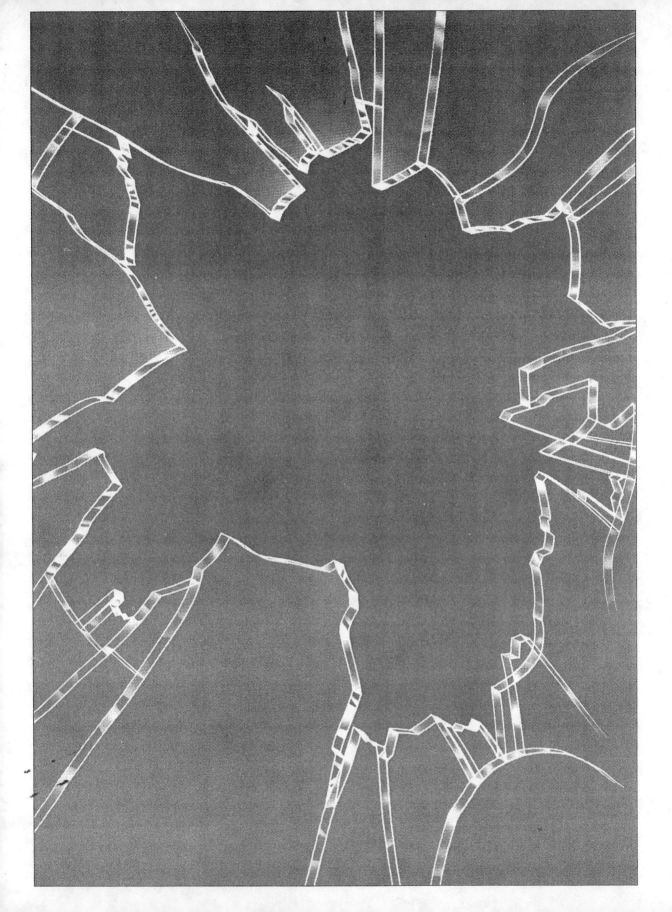

WRITING PROMPT

Uh-oh!

_____

_____

_____

_____

_____

_____

_____

_____

_____

_____

_____

_____

_____

_____

_____

WRITING PROMPT

Someone dropped a wallet.

_____

_____

_____

_____

_____

_____

_____

_____

_____

_____

_____

_____

_____

_____

_____

WRITING PROMPT

I couldn't believe my eyes!

WRITING PROMPT

My Neighborhood

_____

_____

_____

_____

_____

_____

_____

_____

_____

WRITING PROMPT

Shoes tell a lot about a person.

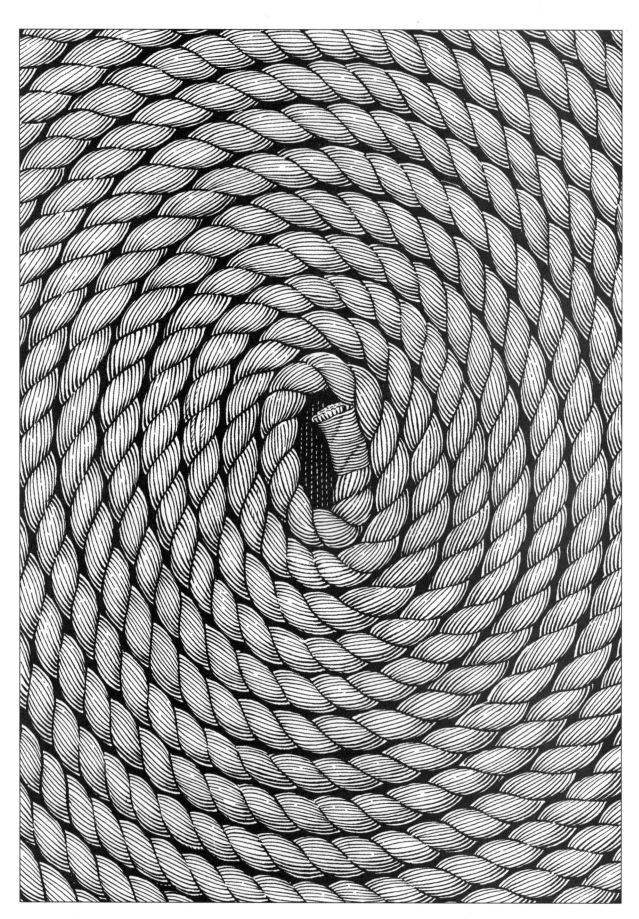

WRITING PROMPT (Write your own.)

WRITING PROMPT

I finally found those keys.

WRITING PROMPT

Cloud Pictures

_____

_____

_____

_____

_____

_____

_____

_____

_____

_____

_____

_____

_____

_____

_____

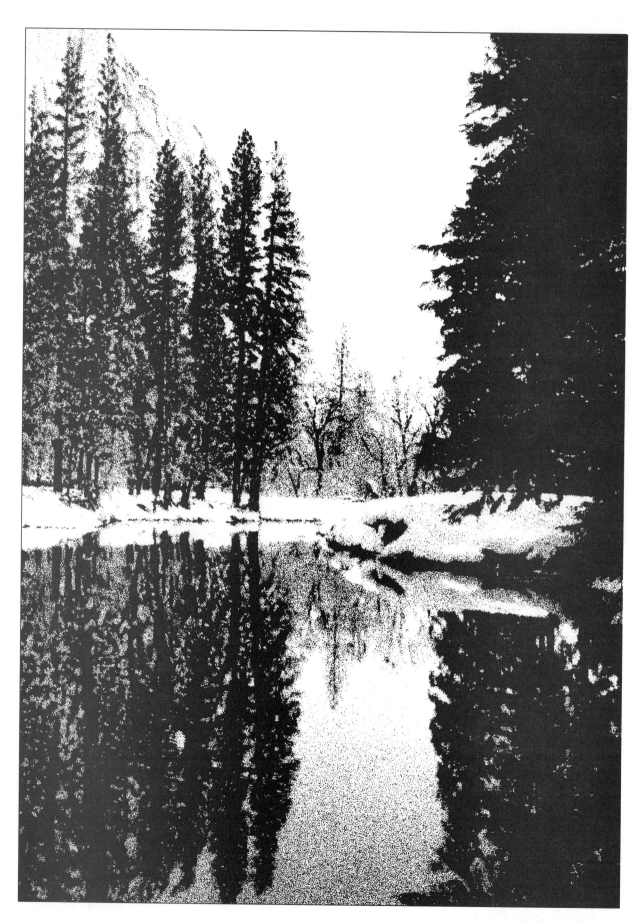

WRITING PROMPT

In winter when it's silent . . .

_____

_____

_____

_____

_____

_____

_____

_____

_____

_____

_____

_____

_____

_____

WRITING PROMPT

On the Coast

_____

_____

_____

_____

_____

_____

_____

_____

_____

_____

_____

_____

_____

Writing Topics
Daily Journal Writing

> "I can tap into [my students'] human instinct to write if I help them realize that their lives and memories are worth telling stories about, and if I help them zoom in on topics of fundamental importance to them."
>
> **—writing teacher JUNE GOULD**

As classroom teachers, we know from firsthand experience that the personal stories young learners love to share can serve as the basis of an effective and lively writing program. Here's how we did it:

Getting Started

At the beginning of the school year, we introduced in-class journal writing to the students. (We encouraged them to write outside of class in journals as well, but the journals in school were part of our writing program.) We knew that the most effective way to get students into writing was simply to let them write often and freely about their own lives, without having to worry about grades or turning their writing in. This helped them develop a feel for "real" writing—writing that originates from their own thoughts and feelings.

That's where the journals come in. Nothing gets students into writing more effectively than a personal journal. (And no other type of writing is so easy to implement.) All your students need are spiral notebooks, pens, time to write, and encouragement to explore whatever is on their minds. (See page 133 in the *Writers Express* handbook for more information.)

We provided our students with four or five personal writing topics each time they wrote. They could use one of these topics as a starting point, or write about something else entirely. The choice was theirs. (We found that providing writing topics was easier and more productive than just saying "You've got plenty to write about.")

Writing Topics

To start off an exercise, we posted suggested writing topics like these:

- your most memorable kitchen-related experience,
- coping with brothers or sisters,
- being home alone, late at night, or
- what you did over the weekend.

Students would either choose from the list or write on a topic they preferred. See pages 141-144 in this booklet for more suggested topics. We asked our students to write every other day for the first 10 minutes of the class period. (Every Monday, Wednesday, and Friday were writing days.) Of course, we had to adjust our schedule at times, but, for the most part, the students wrote three times a week.

Keeping It Going

After everyone was seated and roll was taken, the journals were passed out, the topics were given, and everyone wrote. We expected students to write for a full 10 minutes, nonstop. They knew that they would earn a quarterly journal grade based on the number of words they produced. This almost made a contest out of the writing sessions. Each time they wrote, they wanted to see if they could increase their production from past journal entries, and they always wanted to write more than their classmates.

> "Over the last fifteen years, a number of teachers around the country and their students have been amazed by what happened when people write ten to fifteen minutes without worrying about grammar, spelling, or punctuation, and concentrate only on telling some kind of truth."
>
> **—KEN MACRORIE**

Wrapping It Up

On days that we weren't writing, we shared journal entries. First, each student would exchange journals with a classmate. He or she would count the number of words in the latest entry, read it carefully, and then make comments on things he or she liked or questioned. After each pair had shared their comments with one another, we would talk about the entries as a class.

Many writers themselves would be reluctant to share their entries with the entire class. But the readers had no problem volunteering someone else's entry ("You've got to hear Nick's story") and reading it out loud. The students loved these readings and the discussions that followed.

Personal Experience Papers

Periodically, we would interrupt the normal course of journal writing and sharing and make formal writing assignments. That is, we would ask students to review their entries and select one (or part of one) to develop into a more polished, complete, personal experience paper. Usually, those entries that readers enjoyed and wanted to know more about would be the ones the young writers would choose to develop.

We wanted to make sure that their writing went through at least one or two thorough revisions, so we gave our writers plenty of class time to work on their papers. We also required them to turn in all preliminary work with their final drafts. (See "Writing Personal Narratives," page 138, in the *Writers Express* handbook for guidelines for this type of writing.)

The experience papers were shared with the entire class at the end of the project. This was a fun and informal activity, but one that students came to appreciate as an important part of the entire composing process. It was their day. They were on stage. They were sharing the culmination of all their hard work—a special moment in their own lives.

Writing Topics

Possibilities

- If I could . . .
- If I could have three wishes . . .
- If I could play any instrument . . .
- If I could fly . . .
- If I could climb a mountain . . .
- If I could buy anything . . .
- If I could build a clubhouse . . .
- If I could live anywhere . . .
- If I could visit my hero . . .
- If I could travel back in time . . .

Characterization

- If I were . . .
- If I were incredibly smart . . .
- If I were a superhero . . .
- If I were a teacher . . .
- If I were unable to use my legs . . .
- If I were an animal . . .
- If I were 10 feet tall . . .
- If I were as old as my grandparents . . .

Titles

- A Campfire Tale
- My Grandma the Race Car Driver
- A Mixed-Up Day
- The Broken Alarm Clock
- Timmy the Turtle's Adventure
- Cereal with Mustard on Top
- The Longest Tunnel
- When the Tornado Hit
- My Grandpa the Storyteller

School Life

- A project I worked hard on
- My favorite thing to do at recess
- Waiting for the bus
- I like/dislike singing in our school's spring concert.
- What I do when I get home from school
- My most challenging subject
- I wish our class could take a field trip to . . .

Writing Topics

Me, Myself, and I

- I like/dislike my name because . . .

- When I am 25, this is how my life will be.

- One thing about myself I wish I could change

- The best thing about me

- The best gift anyone ever gave me

- I was really, really looking forward to it, and then . . .

- My most prized possession

- A day of my favorite foods

- I could do this all day long.

Family Life

- Pets in my family

- I wish my family was different.

- This is how I know my parents care about me.

- A typical dinner at my house

- Things I like to do with my parents

- When I visit my grandparents

- My favorite relative

Friends

- A perfect day with my best friend

- Sometimes I wish I could tell my friend . . .

- A time when my friends were mean to me

- The last birthday party I went to

This 'n' That

- I visited the animal shelter and wanted to adopt all the animals!

- If squirrels ruled the world

- I am going to write a book.

- Earthquake!

- I thought I would be grounded for a month.

- A job everyone would like to have

Definitions

- A friend is . . .

- A good vacation is . . .

- A good book is one that . . .

- A playground is . . .

- A father is . . .

- Laughter is . . .

- A computer is . . .

Writing Topics

Nature

- A big fish in a small lake
- Once I saw a . . . in my neighborhood.
- A tree that got hit by lightning
- Should people keep wild animals as pets?
- I know that bats are good to have around, but they give me the creeps!
- One way to be a good citizen of the earth
- I was glad it was raining.
- A sky full of stars

Take Sides

- Year-round school
- Animal rights
- School uniforms/dress codes
- School security
- Video games
- Television/Internet viewing regulations
- Organized sports for elementary grades

Questions

- How are coral reefs being protected?
- How are bridges made?
- What is life like in a submarine?
- What's it like in the kitchen of a zoo?
- How do grocery stores and restaurants get all their fresh food?
- Why don't some kinds of ice cream melt?
- Is it dangerous that the air is filled with microwave communication signals?
- What dog makes the best pet?
- How is vegetable oil made from sunflowers, corn, and peanuts?
- How are subways built?
- How are buildings made to resist earthquakes?
- What are highways made of?
- How do window washers get fresh water on the 50th floor?

Writing Topics

Either/Or

- Would I rather play a sport or be a spectator?

- Would I prefer reading the book or seeing the movie?

- Would I rather climb a mountain or go to a mall?

- Would I choose to ride a horse or a snowmobile?

- Would I rather go snorkeling or spelunking?

- Would it be more fun to go down a white-water river or go on a roller coaster?

- Would I rather explore an ocean beach or a history museum?

- Would I rather play the piano or a set of drums?

- Would I rather sing a song or dance to music?

- Would I rather write a letter or play a video game?

- Would I rather take a photo or draw a picture?

Compare/Contrast

- Metric to American measurements

- Hand tools to power tools

- Meat to vegetables

- Freedom to slavery

- Light to darkness

- Cross-country skiing to snowmobiling

- Mountain climbing to scuba diving

- A house to an apartment

- Being strong to being funny

- Leading to following

- Winning to losing

Show-Me Sentences
Producing Writing with Detail

From time immemorial teachers have said to their students, "Your essay lacks details" or "This idea is too general" or "Show, don't tell." We even know of a teacher who had a special stamp made: "Give more examples."

So how should this problem be approached? It's obvious that simply telling students to add more details and examples is not enough. Even showing them how professional writers develop their ideas is not enough (although this does help). Students learn to add substance and depth to their writing through regular practice.

Here's one method that has worked for many students and teachers: the Show-Me sentences. Students begin with a basic topic—"My locker is messy," for example—and create a paragraph or brief essay that *shows* rather than *tells*. The sentence is a springboard for lively writing.

About Your Show-Me Sentences . . .

The following pages contain 45 Show-Me sentences. Each sentence speaks directly to students, so they should have little difficulty creating essays full of personal details. Again, we suggest that you use these sentences every other day for an extended period of time (at least a month).

Note: By design, each page of Show-Me sentences can be made into an overhead transparency.

Implementation

DAY ONE Before you ask students to work on their own, develop a Show-Me sentence as a class. Start by writing a sample sentence on the board. Then have students volunteer specific details that give this basic thought some life. List their ideas on the board. Next, construct a brief paragraph on the board using some of these details. (Make no mention of the original sentence in your paragraph.) Discuss the results. Make sure that your students see how specific details help create a visual image for the reader. Also have your students read and react to examples of "showing writing" from professional texts. (Share the sample of "showing writing" on page 147 with your students.)

DAY TWO Have students work on their first Show-Me sentences in class. Upon completion of their writing, have pairs of students share the results of their work. Then ask for volunteers to share their writing with the entire class. (Make copies of strong writing for future class discussions.)

DAY THREE Ask students to develop a new paragraph. At the beginning of the *next* class period, discuss the results (break into pairs as before). Continue in this fashion for at least a month.

Note: Reserve the first 5 or 10 minutes of each class period for writing or discussing. (Students who don't finish their writing in class should have it ready for the next day.)

Evaluation

Have students reserve a section in their notebooks for their writing or have them compile their work in a folder. At regular intervals, give them some type of performance score for their efforts. At the end of the unit, have them select one or two of their best examples to revise and then submit for a thorough evaluation.

Enrichment

In *Writers in Training*, Rebekah Caplan developed an extensive program to help students produce well-detailed, engaging essays. She made the following suggestions:

- Have your students turn cliches like *It's a small world* or *Accidents will happen* into strong narrative or descriptive paragraphs.

- Have them develop sentences like *Friday nights are better than Saturday nights* into paragraphs that compare and contrast two subjects.

- In addition, have students convert loaded statements like *Noon hours are too short* or *I don't need a bedtime* into opinion pieces.

Note: In a sense, these variations become progressively more challenging. Most student writers, for example, have more difficulty supporting an opinion than they have illustrating the basic ideas behind a cliche.

- You might also use vocabulary words from science, math, social studies, and so forth, in Show-Me sentences or connect these sentences to literary works under study. (Generally speaking, Show-Me sentences can be linked to any unit of study.)

Sample **Showing Writing**

■ **The twins are different as night and day.** *(cliche)*

Even though Jack and Zack are identical twins, they don't seem to have much in common. Jack wears glasses, and Zack does not. Jack dyed a green streak in his short, spiky hair, while Zack has a crew cut. Jack prefers sweats, but Zack likes jeans and button-down shirts. Their personalities are different, too. Jack is funny and loud. Zack is serious and quiet. They have different friends at school, too.

SHOW-ME SENTENCES

- **The toy was damaged.**

- **The birthday party was fun.**

- **It was raining hard.**

- **My brother can make large bubbles.**

- **The sunset was pretty.**

SHOW-ME SENTENCES

- **I've never been so embarrassed.**

- **This puppy is cute.**

- **I enjoyed myself at the fair.**

- **The bird flew away.**

- **I read a great book.**

SHOW-ME SENTENCES

- **That movie is so funny.**

- **The people next door are noisy.**

- **She looked angry.**

- **The old house seemed mysterious.**

- **Our game ended in victory.**

SHOW-ME SENTENCES

■ **The telephone rang.**

■ **An aardvark is an awkward animal.**

■ **I like the color _____ .**

■ **This old blanket is so comfortable.**

■ **Those burgers tasted awful.**

SHOW-ME SENTENCES

- **Skateboarding is awesome.**

- **The bad weather made them late.**

- **The shrubs are overgrown.**

- **She has a small stuffed animal.**

- **My uncle is one in a million.**

SHOW-ME SENTENCES

- **We had a short vacation.**

- **The siren caught his attention.**

- **The shore was littered.**

- **They had an accident.**

- **Lemons are sour.**

SHOW-ME SENTENCES

- **We always work in a careful manner.**

- **She has beautiful hair.**

- **The night was black as coal.**

- **They dug a deep hole.**

- **He was unusually flexible.**

SHOW-ME SENTENCES

■ **We decorated the room for the party.**

■ **This empty box could be useful.**

■ **The boat floated on the lake.**

■ **_____ is my prized possession.**

■ **Thanksgiving is a pleasant holiday.**

SHOW-ME SENTENCES

- **He doesn't like that food.**

- **She left in a hurry.**

- **My cat is sweet.**

- **He was grouchy.**

- **The elevator moved very slowly.**